Powerlines

New Writing from the Water's Edge

[signature]

Edited by
Dexter Petley

[signature]

TWO RAVENS
PRESS

Published by Two Ravens Press Ltd.
Green Willow Croft
Rhiroy, Lochbroom
Ullapool
Ross-shire IV23 2SF
United Kingdom

www.tworavenspress.com

The right of the editor and contributors to be identified as
authors of this work has been asserted by them in accordance
with the Copyright, Designs and Patent Act, 1988.
Anthology © Two Ravens Press 2009.
For copyright of contributors, see page 179.

ISBN: 978-1-906120-40-5

British Library Cataloguing in Publication Data: a CIP record
for this book can be obtained from the British Library.

Designed and typeset in Sabon by Two Ravens Press.
Cover design by Two Ravens Press.

Printed in Poland
on Forest Stewardship Council-accredited paper.

About the Editor

Dexter Petley is a novelist, translator, editor and angling writer. His four critically acclaimed novels are *Little Nineveh, Joyride, White Lies* and *One True Void*. His translations include *The Fishing Box* by Maurice Genevoix. Dexter lives in a caravan in Normandy, surviving on organic permaculture, mushroom hunting, rainwater, foraging winter fuel and old birds' nests to decorate the wattle sides of his dry toilet. He is the "dp" half of *Letters from Arcadia* on the *Caught by the River* website http://caughtbytheriver.net. His longer angling writing has appeared in *Waterlog* magazine.

Acknowledgements

A version of *Back Waters* by Colin Higgins first appeared on www.purepiscator.com. Versions of David Profumo's contributions have appeared in *Trout and Salmon (The Stepping Stones), The Scotsman (Between Honey and Salt),* and *The Duncan Lawrie Journal (The Wilderness Cure).* Versions of *Carp Horse Bob* and *Bob Down Valium Valley* by Dexter Petley first appeared in *Waterlog* magazine.

For more information about the editor and authors, see
www.tworavenspress.com

Contents

Foreword

The original fishing story pre-dates language itself. In those ancient days, before the advent of carbon rods – or, for that matter, any kind of rods at all – just about everyone went either hunting or fishing, but if a fisherman came back to his cave with a truly exceptional capture, the rest of the tribe would no doubt have allowed him to describe his triumph with a long series of expressive grunts and expansive gestures. And afterwards, perhaps a local artist would have been commissioned to illustrate the story on the cave walls. Fishing stories, therefore, would have been swirling around long before sounds were refined into words.

Formal language inevitably inspired new dimensions of myth and magic and, much later, the written word added complexity and sophistication to the story. However, it's only in the last few generations, when angling with a rod and line became associated as much with meditation as mastication, that the story grew out of its obsession with big chunks of fish and began exploring more interesting backwaters.

The classic fishing story, about an angler's quest for a large or magical fish, has been retold countless times and it seems incredible that after all these thousands of years modern fisherpeople are still happy – nay, positively eager – to listen to or read more of the same. My own angling writing is mostly just variations on the theme and though I like to improvise, experimenting with different notes, I keep getting drawn back to the familiar tune. Dexter Petley, however, is a more natural radical. I have always admired his writing for its original mix of fine-edged description, contemplation and sometimes surreal, brilliant humour. Not only does he include a wonderful example of his style in this book, but he has gone out of his way to reel in other writers who have been wading in their own refreshingly unplummeted waters. The result is a collection of unique, superbly crafted fishing stories, which takes the ancient form to a new and fascinating level.

Chris Yates
Salisbury, Wiltshire

Introduction

When I published my second novel *Joyride*, a lot of people I knew said: oh no, I didn't read it because I know nothing about fishing. This infuriated me for a number of reasons. I wasn't asking anyone to *GO* fishing, was I? My narrator went fishing in the book. He could've been a detective, or a mushroom gatherer or a piano player. Would they have then said: oh no, I didn't read it because I know nothing about detection, mushrooms or pianism? Of course not.

This made me wonder how angling, or writing about angling, had got itself so dislocated, so unconsidered as an accessible literary subject. Since Orwell's *Coming Up For Air*, there have been very few novels which use fishing as definitive narrative conditioners, in that they fix a character, they realise part of the depth of the fictions. Plenty about pianists and painters and all kinds of hobbyists and amateurs who fiddle in inaccessible or autistic occupations, all presented to readers as the givens of fiction and nonfiction alike. In poetry, angling is reserved for the pithy nature poets and usually involves a pike, salmon or an eel. In fiction it's just peek-a-boo and as a subject in nonfiction it is dumped firmly on the field sports and natural worlders. It needs a TV tie-in to elevate it into natural history.

British fiction/nonfiction or literature as a whole, then, absorbs fishing awkwardly, in a way that American or French literature doesn't. Marks of culture, indicating two things: the British are alienated from close contact with nature and their culture has become either urban or too internal; British writers still wear brothel creepers and live in towns. And yet, when you scour the writers' lists, you find plenty of anglers among them. They write, they fish. But as there's no such recognised thing as angling literature, or serious angling writing, there is nowhere much for these writers to go. The British are squeamish readers; fishing is still considered a mucky business for an underclass or the overclass. In the rest of the world it is a natural pursuit with social benefits.

There have been attempts to negotiate some terms. There have been anthologies, some updating previous now dusty Miscellanies and Garlands. But contemporary/living writers are rarely represented. Here and there a journal has stood up to be counted and has given "place" to writing which would otherwise have languished unread, but like all ongoing publications, they are at the mercy of quality, subscription only, and confined within a fishing readership, unable to compete in a big discount marketplace.

And yet, the last few years have seen some mainstreaming of fishing now that it has been adopted as "lifestyle" and not sport. It has entered the world of expensive retro and fashion, the doomed wealthy looking for ways back into "authenticity". The pampered townie yearning for a genuine reason to wear the wellies. Whether good or bad, that has allowed angling writing to creep into prime time, into the lifestyle pages, latch itself onto the trendier nature writing revival, even onto the bestseller lists.

But that is not good enough for those of us who crave real, quality writing. In *Powerlines*, my idea has simply been to gather a dirty neuf on a singular mission. To bring exceptional writing, which just happens to have fishing in it, on it, of it, to readers who crave good contemporary writing of any kind. To collect living novelists, poets, creative nonfiction writers who are also anglers into a single volume. *Powerlines* is the result. Its time has come.

All good anthologies have mission, message and clamour for change and recognition. *Powerlines* is no exception. It does not slip quietly into the swim, it thrashes the waters of the new river. It is broad and deep, and above all exemplifies how angling can observe society in a way non-angling writers cannot. All life is here.

DP
Normandy

Powerlines

John Galligan

John Galligan lives in Madison, Wisconsin, where he works as a college writing instructor, raises two boys, and fly fishes whenever possible. He is the author of a critically acclaimed murder mystery series where the protagonist, an itinerant trout bum, uses his wiles as a fisherman to solve crimes. His books include *The Nail Knot, The Blood Knot* (Crimespree Magazine's 2005 Book of the Year), and *The Clinch Knot* published by Bleak House Books.

He is also the author of *Red Sky, Red Dragonfly,* a novel set in Japan, and *Oh, Brother Said the Mother of Tony Pepperoni,* a children's book.

www.johngalligan.com

The Last Trout

For nearly an hour I had stumbled in pre-dawn darkness up that cold, swift-running Japanese river. Twice I had gone down, hard enough to get my face slapped by snow melt from some high mountain wrinkle.

These were shocking falls. The streams of the midwestern United States, where I was comfortable, were soft-bottomed and bovine in temperament. Fall-ins back home were highly self-conscious affairs: one foot would gradually, irretrievably sink so far into the muck that the tabernacle of the fishing soul would come unbalanced and, in slow motion, dunk itself. But these falls were swift and vicious acts of God. *Bang. Down.* And back up again, breathless, palms stinging, knees throbbing, nose dripping, all the carbon burned out of my nervous system and only one thought left in my head: *there had damn well better be some trout in here.*

My skepticism was well grounded. I had been in Japan for just under two months and had experienced a number of unnerving surprises. Only a few days after my introduction at the English school and my instalment in a barebones apartment near the train station, I had mentioned trout fishing to a curious neighbour. Within minutes I was in this man's Toyota luxury van, packed between his excited twin girls, careening through the steep green mountains of Fukushima Prefecture, passing up what seemed to be miles of glorious trout country in order to stop at last beside a concrete pond brimming with mouldy rainbows that could be caught by six-year-olds with unbaited hooks. What could I do? We new angling friends proceeded in a whirlwind of clattering bamboo poles and flying barbs. Trout thus extracted flipped across dirty gravel ahead of eager hands until Papa put his foot on their heads. We consumed those poor lost souls on the spot, charcoal roasted, and I was forced – forced, I tell you – to drink too much sake.

I pondered this in the coming days as I settled in to my teaching job. I dreamed of all that pretty water, my imagination installing big trout in those black corners and emerald depths. When I could stand it no longer, I purchased a bicycle, and a backpack for my rod and tackle. I rode out every morning, before classes, and I searched as far as one hundred-kilometre round-trips on weekends. But my investigations revealed to me a horror: nearly every body of water that I had admired for its muscle and wit turned out, up close, to be little more than a vigorous irrigation ditch, the charming puppet of some blunt upriver dam.

I was jilted, dumbfounded, and finally outraged. I was a much younger man then, full of ideas, unseasoned by disenchantment, utterly un-mentored and effectively alone in the world. Indignant, I stewed in gaijin isolation. What kind of place was this? Why, in fact, had I come here? A certain dread began to overtake me as I understood I was surrounded by all that lovely dead water. Far from impressing people with my fly fishing, far from using anything so familiar as both a calling card and a comfort, I was riding around an alien countryside like a jackass, like some unrequited Johnny Appleseed, a white hairy monster dangling flies into ditches while farmers looked on, frightened and appalled.

Then I took a desperate excursion to Okawa, the big, braided and obviously messed-up river that runs between concrete bumpers through the centre of the Aizu valley, where I had observed dozens of fishermen in what appeared to be water-skiing gear wielding twenty-foot poles. I quickly discovered to my compounding bewilderment that every one of them, for miles on end, had a fish on – a fish that no fisherman was making the slightest effort to land. Hammering away with my blunt Japanese, I cobbled together an explanation: each of those fish was storebought, a small, vegetarian, territorial fish called the aiu, available for purchase at the local tackle shop. The plan from there was to harness that little aiu inside a halo of hooks, swing it out into the current, and hope it swam into the territory of another aiu (they were heavily stocked). That free-range aiu, thus violated, would attack and get snagged in the other's constellation of hooks. This new fish would be summarily landed (the aiu did not struggle), kept in a live well, and generally sold back to the store for credit. Understandably, such a sport required vast amounts of alcohol and hot sun – and most of the fishermen, I eventually realized, were wearing rubber suits. Of course.

At my place of work – the school was itself a dim and fallow dissolution of my ideal – I was noisy with my sorrows, bitter in my inquisition. These were conversation classes, and this was my conversation. Horrible crimes against nature had been committed. These crimes continued unchecked as we sat over our text books learning 'big' and 'small' and 'left' and 'right.' My brain could not slow down for this. I tried to explain: more than any place I had ever been, Japan was a paradise lost. So much perfect wild habitat had been spoiled in the last fifty years – I claimed this anyway, waxing hyperbolic for educational purposes – that I could still hear the screaming and the moaning as I biked through cement-slathered road cuts, as I climbed denuded mountain slopes, as I coasted down entire expiring watersheds intubated with sluice and culvert and ditch. How could this happen? Who was responsible? Didn't anyone care or even notice? Wasn't there some clean and natural stream that I could fish? Blank looks. Lowered heads. Crazy, scary, time's up. *Wild*.

Naturally I began to booze a bit and wander the streets at night, trying to understand the deception, the emptiness. Water had always been good to me. It had always been a place to go for reassurance, for mystery and adventure, and most of all to receive the awe of nature that seemed to fuel my enjoyment of life. And here, in Japan, water flowed everywhere. Any place I went, I heard gurgling under the city. I felt water's cool breath rising through roadside grates. Every way I turned there was another river, another bridge, and when I stood beside guard rails at night and listened to the invisible currents below, I would fill back up with hope and with the overpowering thrill of moving, living water. There had to be trout around somewhere, I told myself.

Then, one night on the edge of my despair, a teak-skinned

man of young middle age turned up in my intermediate English class and sat quietly for an hour or so, watching and listening as I tried unsuccessfully to explain my own grammar. Afterwards, he put a small plastic box in my hand. My heart leapt. I could tell from the faint chuff and rattle that the box contained dry flies. 'My name,' he said, 'is Sato,' he said. 'Would you,' he said, 'care,' he said, 'to join me,' he said, 'to drink?'

We spelunked into a dark and musty basement jazz bar, gulped Kirin beer from big bottles poured into tiny glasses. A friend of a client's brother's wife was in one of my classes, Sato explained with considerable difficulty, and in this small-town manner, word of my problem had reached him.

He was a fly fisherman himself, Sato went on. He lit a cigarette and topped my beer. He deployed his limited English with patience and care. Yes, he tied his own flies. Yes, he practiced catch-and-release. Either sixteen, six, or sixty years ago – here he struggled a bit – his title-search business solidified and his future became secure. He decided to take up fly fishing.

So far so good. A Coltrane LP spun and popped behind the bar. The shaggy-haired barkeep, Sato's friend, bowed and smiled encouragingly, socked in amidst his massive collection of jazz on vinyl. Sato kept my beer on an aggressive refresh programme.

So how had my new friend come to learn fly fishing? He had caught the bullet train, he told me, and made a pilgrimage to Tokyo, where he had presented himself, unannounced, to a flycasting 'master' he had read about in a sporting magazine. This man was busy, Sato said, so he waited. The man was evasive. Sato persisted. The man asked for many thousand yen. Sato paid. He then was let inside the man's garden gate, and over a narrow, gummy casting pond, between high rises in the middle of Tokyo, Sato studied the art of casting a fly under a man he described to me as a 'so-so fisherman but a great teacher.' He claimed to have learned muscle movement, line control, breathing, balance, concentration, and patience. He claimed to have learned knots. He learned, he claimed, about duns and emergers and pupae and larvae. He said he asked questions, listened to fish stories, and sat in silent meditation. He was commanded to build his own rod. At the end of those few days, Sato told me, he and the master drank together. The master fell into the pond and needed Sato to pull him out. Sato had purchased his rod-building supplies the next morning and caught the train back home, and from that moment forward he was a fly fisherman.

I was gulping beer at this point. The story made me nervous for so many reasons, but in no small measure because Sato had related it with no apparent discomfort, as if his experience were the most natural thing in the world.

Then: how did I learn to fly fish?

Hours upon hours in the Idaho Rockies, I told him, on the Snake and the Lochsa and the Clearwater, with a salmon egg on a Zebco, then later as an adolescent with a box of spinners, taking Dolly Varden in the alpine lakes of the Cascades, and finally as a driven and solitary young adult, teaching myself by hard trial and copious error to inveigle German brown trout with a fly rod on the spring creeks of Wisconsin.

'Ah,' said Sato behind a cloud of smoke. 'I see.'

He restored my beer. The barkeep shot me a nod, tilted Monk's *Straight, No Chaser* onto the turntable. Sato leaned through his smoke. Here it came.

'So what,' he said, 'do you think?' he said. 'Shall we,' he said, 'go fishing?'

Splash! Bang! Down a third time I went in that icy, treacherous water.

This time I wet both of my sleeves to the shoulder. As I struggled up, dripping and cussing, I was all too mindful of my earlier reversals. Sure, Sato and I had left my apartment parking lot at four a.m. and driven almost two hundred kilometres, far beyond the range of my bicycle. But after all that, wasn't I still fishless, and hauling myself back upright by an iron cleat inside a concrete stream bank? Hadn't Sato fallen behind, nearly an hour ago, because he had heard a generator chug to life back in the tiny village and decided to move his car before some farmer glazed it with pesticide? Don't get your hopes up, I was telling myself.

But up my hopes came anyway, with the light of day, and only moments later. There I was, shaking and shivering, actually bleeding now from one elbow, when abruptly sunlight sprayed across some mountain's broad crown and swirled down into that little valley, gilding the fruit-laden persimmon trees and the blue tin rooftops and the frog-croaking patchworks of bristling, bright green rice. On cue came a flurry of bumps against my waters. Quick, solid, panic-stricken bumps.

There, I told myself.

Trout!

But where was Sato? Behind me now that little river coursed away downstream in misty sunlight between concrete walls that were scored in an argyle pattern and hung with dewy twists of kudzu. Somewhere a mini tractor snarled and popped, warming up. Those throaty Japanese crows had started to converse, the relentless pigeons too, and I could smell a distant trash fire. But Sato? No sign of the man.

I did not know yet what to make of my guide. The night before, he and I had met a second time at a tavern called American Ragtime, to make our plans. This was a meeting to which Sato attached tremendous importance, choosing the venue as carefully as if he were choosing a fly to match a hatch. But if American Ragtime were to be a fly in my box, it would be the goofus bug. Ragtime was not a Gershwin-era theme, as it turned out, but rather an attractive English word plucked at random from the strange gusts of Western culture that blow through Japan. The décor was a self-serious salad of Americana: everything from antique washboards and watering cans to posters of Bart Simpson and Rachel Welch, all of this lit by the bloody hues of a dubbed Chuck Norris movie playing on the television. Most worrisomely, though, it seemed to be Sato's earnest misimpression of the kind of place I would like to go. We sat at a table beneath a giant Coke bottle cap nibbed under with a light bulb. Recalling the aiu fishermen, I readied myself to hear the plan: *step one, go to trout store, buy trout.* Was this where Sato had gone earlier? Had he driven to the local trout store? Was he upstream, now, bowling fish at me?

But I steadied myself in body and mind. After all there was some reason to hope – or at least to remain hopeful about Sato. After slurping down his soba at American Ragtime, he had withdrawn several sheets of paper from his briefcase. 'Please,' he said, 'research,' he said, 'my plan.'

He handed me what could have passed for a work of folk art: a two-page timetable in flowchart form, beginning with a three a.m. pickup at my apartment, placing us in the water before sunup, offering various entertaining permutations through the hot and unfishable midday, with all paths leading back to three hours of evening fishing. Attached were breakfast and lunch menus. Interspersed among the text were sketches of flies, tackle, and trout. There were photocopies for me.

I was impressed. We raised our glasses.

'Three a.m.!'

'Three a.m.!'

We must have done it over ten more times.

But after all that build-up, Sato had not arrived at three a.m., nor at any other time close to our excitedly appointed hour.

At 2:55, executing manoeuvres in a groggy no-man's land between the night before and the morning after, I had routed myself from the futon, shouldered my knapsack, gripped my rod tube, locked my apartment door, and gone outside to wait in the parking lot. I would be the last one to dam up the flowchart.

It was a cool, humid morning, with a single cloud snagged on the blade of a sickle moon. I listened in vain for the approach of Sato's car. I paced. I re-checked the schedule. Finally I settled down on the asphalt amidst the compact cars and scooters and mini-pickups and listened to my neighbours vomit.

This sound, too regular to dismiss, had been one stiff

early test of my ability to understand and adjust. My leadoff observation was that many Japanese – young businessmen especially – worked like wind-up toys for ten hours or more, then drank with artless abandon until they had just enough wits left to pound down a huge bowl of ramen soup and make a run for home. The aftermath, in a country of open windows and thin walls, was a nighttime chorus so visceral, so creepily intimate, that I felt a raw animal kinship with my neighbours, a forced and repulsive closeness that did not comport with their distance and propriety by day. I had begun to sense there was something in this that connected to water.

The week of my arrival in Japan, I had spent my jet lag hours roaming streets that were narrow and deliberately labyrinthine to forestall 19th-century invaders en route to the city's castle heart. As far as I could tell, the city still baffled its share of gladiators: executives in expensive suits down dead ends, pants open and eyes shut, pissing; office ladies in shimmering make-up teetering knock-kneed in the middle of traffic, throwing up into hankies; young salarymen, software engineers by day, sleeping it off in doorways and alleys, unable to execute the chain of commands required to get home. And now, as three or four distinctive retches echoed across the quadrangle of tiny, uniform apartments, I recalled Sato bidding me good night outside a second tavern door, down the alley from Ragtime. Somehow I knew I was in for a long wait.

So I stretched out on the warm asphalt and settled uneasily into an analysis of what I had been supposing was a pivotal Japanese contradiction: the rigour, the discipline, and the intricate aesthetic of the day, followed by the gut-wrenching howl of the night. I knew that this paradox in itself was normal enough. This was a facet of the human condition that could be appreciated, here in Japan, for its frankness and its clean lines of definition. But the mysterious and troubling thing for me so far had been the lack of discernible tension between the two extremes. In my culture, there was socialized man and there was unhinged beast. True, they might be one in the same creature, but getting from one to the other required some ugly and lengthy footage, in permutations from Stevenson's *Strange Case of Dr. Jekyll and Mr. Hyde* to any number of versions of *The Fly.* The unsightliness, pain, and complication of the transition served to stigmatize the beast, I thought; or at the very least, all that drama demonstrated a fearful awareness of inner conflict, of the essentially terrible ironies of human existence.

But to my outsider's eye there were no signs of such awareness in Japan. All the irony around my observations seemed to be self-supplied. This was a culture where people thronged to ancient Shinto shrines and prayed fervently and without self-consciousness for auto safety, good grades, and favourable interest rates. This was country – and now I was getting back to my problem with fishing – where a man could speak passionately of his country's natural beauty, could proudly and accurately show it off to a visitor, then pull his Toyota mini-van to the side of the highway and empty his ashtray. There seemed to be, deep in the Japanese psyche, a well-greased pivot point between aversive extremes, a wrinkle in the human soul that allowed a tolerance for contradiction that I did not possess. And this cognitive flip-flopping, this apparent ability to ignore discord and discount shame – I found this disturbing. I found it impossible. I did not see the path and could not accept the result. Sato was now an hour late. His plan was paper only. As the neighbour above me directed another chunky yodel into his toilet bowl, I worked up a predisposition, I admit, for the charade of the day ahead.

But now: *Trout!*

My body tightened, my eyes narrowed. I glanced back once more for Sato, then put the man out of my mind as superfluous. I was into some fish here.

The hackles on my fly glistened as I tossed it on the rising breeze and commanded a size twelve Adams, my yeoman in those days, across ten metres of suddenly trout-charmed water. Never mind the argyle-patterned concrete sluice and the tang of pesticide on the breeze. I was into some damn fish.

Nothing rose right away, but I knew how to make a good thing of that. Work a little, change flies, wade with greater stealth – that was the beauty of my craft. After a half-dozen casts with a smaller, wiser fly, I heard a hefty splash from the upstream dimness. I next felt a flurry of solid bumps against my waders. Good God, I thought. My heart began to thump like a shoe in a dryer. This place is *infested* with trout!

I stepped into a new foothold among the slippery rocks and cast ahead to a corner where nighttime lingered and where the riprap had cracked and sprouted long, limp grass. As my fly floated back under dewy grass noggins, I felt a single, heavy bump, this one crotch-high in the water, strangely soft and lingering. My eye remained on the fly ahead, but I was distracted. That big soft trout just hung there at my privates. This felt wrong. Sooner than I meant to, I picked up my fly and snagged it in the grass. The trout drifted away, but now I was hung up.

I yanked and wiggled and strategized how to save my fly, and as I did so, the sky shifted and the bright light of morning moved like a slide-wipe over the river's concrete banks. Suddenly I could see through the complex surface and down to the river's round, gray bottom stones. I could see what was wrong, too. I was awash in a flotilla of garbage. The 'trout' I had been spooking from their holes were nothing more remarkable – or less remarkable, take your pick – than a few of the many dozen mouldy eggplant drifting and spinning around me. The big trout hung up between my legs had been a cucumber, a real lunker, nearly two feet long. Toward me now floated a plastic Seven-Eleven bag, puffed like a jellyfish. I cursed appallingly. I grabbed at this most egregious piece of litter, and as I did so, I slipped and fell for the fourth time that morning, feeling once more the hard shock of water and stone, but also this time, about the head and neck, the trout-like caress of additional eggplant.

And where the hell was Sato by now? Out emptying his ashtray?

I should confess something here. Put the classic picture of a gentleman fly fisher in your mind. Now put it out. I was not this man then and never will be. I am an athlete and a hard-driven, hard-nosed, competitive bastard who goes into second base head first. I can scarcely contain this in daily life, can narrowly endure polite society. No surprise that I am a feisty fly caster who seeks challenge. I have the skills and tools of that chap you pictured a moment ago, but I am not afraid to be inelegant. In fact I prefer mud, mosquitoes, and impossible casting scenarios. I am a bushwhacker and a trespasser. I explore. I discover. Never am I happier than when hunkered like a troll over some cryptic riffle off the mental map of the fly fishing cognoscenti, celebrating with solitary obscenities as a wild trout twists in my grip. I live for that. I'll fish until it's too cold to move or dark to see, and I'll not be chatting later at the tailgate over ripe cheeses and fine cigars. I'll be necking down beers alone in the dark somewhere and plotting tomorrow. I will die by drowning or by driving my car off the road while looking at water. I accept all this. I have staked out this ground. *Mine.*

All this to explain why I didn't throw down my rod right there. Determined to extract a trout from this flowing ratatouille, I fished on. I oiled my fly. I moved my feet and cast. Again, again. The eggplant kept coming for a while and then gave way to other food groups, most notably a peck or so of crow-damaged tomatoes, one of which I snagged and then sidearmed to slush against the riprap wall. I was laughing now, but sourly. I fished right up to the farmer tipping another wheelbarrow load over the edge, slopping in a potpourri of moulded soybean pods and daikon rinds, plus the odd vending machine coffee can.

'Good morning,' called this wee terror, in his tall rubber boots and his barnacle-shaped straw hat.

Grunt.

'Fishing, eh?'

Growl.

I zinged a pointed cast above the arc of his effluence. He

grinned back at me with huge gold-rimmed teeth. 'Good luck!'

Upstream, I tried to regroup. I presumed that above these desecrations the river would recover. The fishing would finally begin. But then, bobbing half-submerged down the next riffle, arrived an empty three-litre Sapporo Beer mini-keg. I grimly fished it out. For lack of a better idea, I hung the dripping barrel from my back suspender button. When I looked up from this tricky manoeuvre, the river had abruptly turned colour. The current was opaque with ash, marl, industrial waste, something. It was grey-brown, nearly unrecognizable as water, gushing like a leak from some horrid upstream train wreck. And there, over the bubbling sweep ahead, stood my guide, my master, Sato.

Of course, looking back, I had in some measure been set up for vexation by my own mistaken assumptions. But one can hardly help processing the images of bonsai cultivation, tea ceremony, flower arrangement, haiku, exquisite temple gardens, and cherry blossom festivals without concluding that the Japanese have a deep reverence for nature. I know that in my young and eager mind I had correlated these activities with the lovely intricacies of fly fishing and the unsurpassed elegance of trout. I can still recall looking out the window as my Japan Air flight banked over eastern Honshu – seeing all that vibrant green down there, all that water – and having a troll moment right there in window seat 234D. *Here we go. Sonofabitch. Right here, baby. Fly fishing paradise.*

But I was at least fifty years too late, and such paradise as may have once existed, I soon understood, had been only what paradise so often is: a temporary economic oversight, just off the exploitation radar. What I would learn that first summer and in the many years afterward is that Japan's natural ecosystems, every conceivable facet therein, had been leveraged to serve a post-war environmental Armageddon that had taken every tree and dammed every river and strewn a carnage of extinctions and industrial poisonings and preposterous eyesores across the entire five islands. The only big timber remaining was protected on sacred temple grounds. The last unpaved mountainsides were simply too steep for machinery. Deer and pigs had largely vanished. Bears when encountered were promptly shot. Even rabbits were rare. By the time I made it to the veritable frontier of Hokkaido, the famous fox had diminished to a tourist trinket, a kind of local Hello Kitty.

But it was basic foodstuffs, above all, that seemed to clinch my understanding of the true estrangement of Japanese from nature. I watched apple growers pitch pointed ladders into their trees and climb to wrap each and every nascent fruit in a special paper bag to protect it from anything that might naturally happen to an apple as it grows. These same apples would appear later in a supermarket at three dollars a pop, polished and coddled in individual soft-foam jockstraps. There were no roadside stands or U-Pick-Em orchards. Never. Anywhere. No one wanted that. Why? Because nature, even at that level, was dangerous, dirty, and inconvenient. This fetish for disconnected food, I came to think, was another level of the daytime-nighttime paradox that so perplexed me. There was the sheen of day – the image of the noble farmer, tilling the soil, upholding tradition, feeding the people – and then there was the retching, staggering, unmentionable night – exhausted, over-utilized soil that reeked of chemical fertilizers; massive and indiscriminate pesticide application; ridiculous prices propped up by government – and then again, dayside, with no perceptible stress, there was that flawless Fuji apple in perfect slices on the tea tray. And to bring it back to water, there was the farce of aiu fishing, of the great outdoorsman in his rubber suit with his store-bought fish, heroically astream all the hot day long, while the truth was a quiet but monstrous ugliness called 'watershed fragmentation.' Every river, every mountain stream, every rivulet was dammed – not once, but repeatedly, at regular internals, pro forma, for flood control and irrigation, sometimes in anticipation of things that would never happen, often in support of things that had half-happened and fully failed, feats of engineering and hard labour that were sometimes as stunning in their way as pyramid building but for the scantest of purposes and always nearsighted and temporary because without fail these mountain dams filled up with rocks and sand until water flowed straight over the top. A dozen times before I met Sato I had ditched my bike in a bamboo thicket and bushwacked a river high into untravelled realms, climbing hand-over-hand and rod-in-teeth up metal cleats on corroding dam faces, achieving the next level of trespass and thinking that above here there *cannot* be more pointless dams and there *must* be trout. But I had yet to out-hike the dam-building crews. It pissed me off. And it pissed me off that no one else seemed pissed off but me. And there ahead of me, like nothing was the matter, loitered Sato.

My new acquaintance observed me with an unreadable smile. He stood at near attention, his legs together, feet out, narrow shoulders squared, his exquisite rod vertical at his side and his cigarette pointing away from his baggy waders – Chaplinesque.

I jabbed my rod at the chowder coursing around my feet. 'What's going on?'

'There is,' he said, 'a festival,' he said.

I could not find another question to ask. I squished after Sato across a levee between rice paddies. Frogs bailed left and right. Dragonflies careened over the nodding rice spikelets. There was Sato's Honda. He had folded a towel across my seat to keep his upholstery dry and clean. *He should see my car* was all I could think as we pulled away. *He ought to see a real fishing mobile.*

In a kilometre or so the road became narrowed by vehicles parked haphazardly into rice paddies on either side. Soon after we reached the downstream terminus of another village where smack in the middle of the river toiled a backhoe, stirring up a silty, chalky mud. *More government works* I groused aloud as we squeezed past. But as we drew even, I noticed there were no khaki uniforms or hardhats, no emblems of the state, no survey sticks. The backhoe operator had a rag around his head and a beer between his knees. Observed by an eager crowd and guided by two characters tipsily wading the shallows in cheap business suits, the operator was piling cobble in a crude circle to make a pond that spanned and leakily dammed the river. This pond, I gathered, was the focus of the festival.

Sato found a place to park on the perimeter of a graveyard another kilometre ahead. We walked back, Sato managing to explain that the river had been dammed because the village was holding its annual trout fishing derby. The pond would be stocked. Everyone would catch, grill, eat trout, and be merry. My face flushed. My hopes sank to sarcasm. *Great*, I thought. *Sato has found the fish.*

As we arrived, the river remodelling was completed. I sputtered at Sato as the backhoe cleated up ramps onto a flatbed truck. 'Can they *do* that?' Sato was noncommittal. A different truck had rear-ended the new shape of the river. Someone shouted, 'Oy!' Suddenly a gout of water escaped the truck's tail and the pond began to swirl with frantic trout. Just as quickly, the villagers ringing the pond activated long bamboo poles, lobbed in baited hooks. Not thirty seconds later a small rainbow vaulted above the pond, kinking in the sun. That little trout kept rising, seemed to be flying, until it cleared the villagers entirely and plummeted into the dust behind, writhing at the end of an old man's line.

This old man skidded down the dam edge and pounced drunkenly. Grinning, he raised his dust-spackled catch and hollered, 'Mama!' Forward waddled a ruddy old woman built like a squash. She made short work of the trout, ended its life with a rock to the head, slit its belly, disembowelled it in a single motion, flipped the guts toward a cat that had stalked in, and then, the picture of gold-toothed joy, she carried the victual to one of several oil drums hot with snapping, smoking charcoal. But as she laid the trout across the mesh grill, my gaze was captured by the scene beyond her. There, just downstream of the first, another dam had taken shape, this one in miniature to stop up the trickle from the main dam. The purpose of this small dam was to retain water for chilling cans of beer. A stocky, sun-browned young man was all knees and elbows over cardboard cases of Asahi Super Dry, shredding them with great vigour, dumping the beer cans into his little pond, then rising woozily, lighting the empty cardboard over the adjacent barrel and sailing it ablaze into the river.

'Oy!' he kept yelling. 'Oy! Who is going to drink?'

I turned to Sato in a tempest of indignation, neck tendons stilting beneath my head.

'What the hell?'

Sato was composed, prim with a cigarette. 'I believe,' he said, 'we should fish,' he said, 'upstream,' he said, 'of this point.'

We circumnavigated the trout fishing festival and flanked each other up a broad, channelized stretch of the river, flipping caddis fourteens onto obviously fallow water. For a silent two hours, I kept Sato in the corner of my vision. I wrestled with complete disillusionment now. I composed flabbergasted indictments of the pupil and his master. Where was the *spiritual* teaching, I wanted to say. Could it be that by donning his fancy outerwear and rigging his tackle, Sato had satisfied himself? Where was the fervour, the defence of the wild rivers that validated the entire fly fishing experience? On top of that, this man beside me had a peculiar casting stroke. He fished with his rod high, hesitating daintily on the backcast and then stroking down dramatically, like an orchestra conductor invoking tympani. At the end of this stroke, Sato's fly alit, floated high and quick, and then not a metre of drift later he executed a kind of now-give-me-strings pickup, repeated that precious little pause on the backcast, and then demanded more kettle drums.

I might have focused my increasingly sceptical eye on this, but my own casting had become suddenly and horridly ineffective. I was shooting forty feet of line straight ahead and for my efforts getting a miasmic drift where the line snaked and dragged and collided with itself and dunked the fly and hauled it around underwater like a tiny toy duck on a string. The cause of this, I belatedly realized – somewhere in the second hour – was the onrush of water that was both faster and more complex than I was accustomed to fishing. In this stretch of the river, every square metre of the river had its own rules. My forty feet was like asking my line to play chess, rugby, and billiards, all at the same time. It took me a good while longer to recognize that after all Sato had it right with his maestro-stroke. After all, I allowed, he knew *something*. He was fishing one hundred, two hundred different rivers, each on its own terms, one at a time, each about the size of a carpet sample. Not that the Tokyo technique produced any trout, however. For that, actual trout would have to be present. But all morning there was not one inkling of our prey, and Sato insisted we stop for lunch with the skunk still in the bag.

Here is another thing about me, especially true in those raw days. I do not much stop for lunch. I do not feel hungry, generally, while fishing, and I rarely stop without some degree of mastery over the stream, or at the very least without a grip on some small thread of success. I gnaw tobacco, I grow tunnel vision, and my organs are on their own. Extrapolate, I suppose, and you've hit on my scorched-earth approach to life. In any case, I was confounded, secretly appalled, to discover that in our unrequited condition not only would we stop for lunch, but we were going to take the time to light the little stove Sato produced from his rucksack and cook the spaghetti that came out after.

Sato sensed something. 'Don't you like spaghetti?'

'Sure. Yeah. Why not?'

Recalling the flowchart, the menu, I flopped down where Sato established his kitchen on a checkered mat in the shade of a cypress. My head buzzed from the fast water. My jaw hurt. I pushed my hat off and tried to breathe deeply. I stared at that blurring river, tried to understand what I was feeling. It had been nearly two months now since I had stepped off that plane with my fly rod and my English. I was learning my way around

19

now, supposedly becoming more comfortable. But the truth was that I knew far less than when I arrived. I was unlearning, descending into some kind of systemic chaos, comfort draining away. My English, my fly rod – these had turned out to be such weird and fruitless instruments. My surroundings – the sub-tropical flora, the whooping bird sounds, the dim reek of hot forest – had turned so abruptly and surpassingly strange. Upon my arm alit a nozzled, venomous-looking insect that I had never seen before and hoped never to see again. A kind of nameless dread crept in as I watched Sato's rucksack produce additionally a can of Chef Boyardee meat sauce, a can opener, chopsticks, two small aluminium bowls, a litre of bottled water. Out of Sato's rucksack came a head of iceberg lettuce, a bottle of Kraft French dressing, and two tall cans of Budweiser. Of course this was for me, the American, meant to counter the very anxieties of the moment, but it all looked so bizarre.

'It's okay that they do that to the river?' I had swallowed half the beer. 'Dam it up? Throw trash in it? Ruin it for everybody downstream?'

Sato shrugged. 'Mmmm,' he said. 'Perhaps.' His water was near boiling. He passed me a bowl of lettuce under bright orange dressing. Soon I was lifting salad with chopsticks.

'But come on, Sato-san. As a fisherman, don't you care?'

He shrugged again, a smaller motion, just visible.

'That doesn't bother you, back there?'

'Not,' he said, 'so much,' he said.

I gaped at him. He stirred noodles and smoked. I gulped at my beer. I clung to my outrage. How could it fail to matter that we had come all this way and seen what we had seen but not a single native trout? Was Sato going to placidly stir spaghetti while his world went completely to hell? Should I understand that he and his master at the Tokyo casting pond were all about form, appearance – quality attire and proper casting – and a good drunk? Was this how the rivers of Japan would rush to their imminent expirations?

'You mean because the river is already dead – that's why it doesn't bother you?'

Sato squinted through steam as he methodically strained noodles with the pot lid. As starchy water seared the earth, up rose the ripe stench of humus. Then he opened the can of meat sauce with his pocket knife. He poured the sauce over the noodles. He said, 'Please?' and I passed him my salad bowl. Sato filled it with spaghetti. He began to slurp from his own bowl, inhaling a sizeable hank of noodles with each breath. At mid-meal he cleared his throat, wiped his lips with a napkin, paired his chopsticks across the top of his bowl. He lit a cigarette.

'I,' he said, 'bother,' he said.

'You do?'

'Once,' he said, 'I bought,' he said, 'egg.'

'You bought egg?'

'Egg,' he said, 'of trout,' he said.

'And?'

There followed a curious story from three or four years back wherein Sato had presented himself at a trout hatchery and bewildered the management by negotiating the purchase of several hundred fertilized eggs. At home he designed a box for the eggs that allowed water to flow through. This he carried high into the mountains above Aizu-Wakamatsu along some tributary of the Okawa. He anchored the box in a riffle, he said, and hiked back home.

'Did it work?'

'*Wakanai*,' he said. He didn't know.

'You went back to check?'

'The box,' he said, 'was washed,' he said, 'away.'

'But you tried.'

'Yes.'

'May I see your dictionary?' I thumbed the pages back and forth, searching for an accurate way to put it. There was *naïve*. There was *well-intentioned*. There was *ardent*. There was *ridiculous*. But I settled my index finger under this word: *quixotic*.

Sato studied the Japanese. He said, 'Ah!' and then he laughed for a good long time. In fact he seemed so content with the Cervantes characterization that I was moved to challenge him with a story of my own.

'The habitat comes first,' I told him. 'The land. The watershed. Usage. And protecting habitat, taking it back – that amounts to a war.'

Now I told Sato a story. A few years back I had been fishing ahead of a thunderstorm, hearing a tractor and smelling manure all day. Ripe cow flop and ozone too, and when at last the creek rounded up between the farmer's fields, there was the man on his tractor, pulling his spreader, flinging cow shit far and wide under a roiling, rain-heavy sky. Furious, I slung my rod ashore and slogged across that heavy, foetid dirt. The farmer saw me coming but kept his head down until I staggered in front of his tractor. We had an argument then, a shouting match, about whether the coming deluge would wash all that manure into the creek and kill the trout – and about whose creek, whose water, and whose trout those were anyway. It was all his, the farmer claimed, and to do with as he pleased. There were laws, I countered, and fines for abusers of the public trusts in air and water. Get the hell off my land, he told me. Keep your shit out of my water, I shot back. Then the storm came, and later the fish kill. A friend and I returned to the creek a few days later, found a fat dead trout – a big brown, putrefying – and put it in the guy's mailbox.

Sato was laughing at this in an awkward way, cross-legged in his waders, open-mouthed and gasping, smoke leaking upward, a kind of stricken amusement. He asked for his dictionary. His thumbs worked back and forth. He showed me *uncouth*.

Now I laughed. Fine. I took the dictionary back. *Essential*, I gave him.

Counterproductive, he replied.

As opposed – I thumbed in a passion – to *irrelevant*?

While Sato considered the definition, I waved my arm and told him that *this* – sterile water – *this* was what you got when you didn't fight back, when you just blew money on pretty, symbolic gestures. He remained amused. *Tool*, he showed me next, after a long, chuckling search through the impossibly dense pictographs of his language. And *community*, he showed me. This river was a *community tool*.

Capitulate, was my answer. And *short-sighted*. And *life force*.

To which Sato, now convulsive with his silent laugh, struck under with a thumbnail *confrontational* and *overdo* and I marked back *urgent* and *delicate* and *precarious*.

Difficult, was Sato's answer.

Responsible, was mine.

Enjoy, he said.

Defend, I replied.

Complex came back.

Obvious, that triggered from me.

Sato geeked out smoke between his teeth. This last word, it seemed, was sorely funny. He picked up a dry cypress scale and coned his cigarette ash to a sharp red point. Quickly then, he paged his dictionary to the word *adequate*.

'Adequate?' My voice matched bird-shrill from the forest. This word, this man, this place – I was so perplexed. 'But Sato-san, we haven't caught a single fish! We haven't even seen one. I fished through a garbage storm. And we walked right past a crime on nature! What of anything has been adequate today? I might as well have stayed in bed.'

At this, Sato released one last gasp of laughter and then abruptly sobered. He pinned his cigarette to the earth between his boots, then tucked the butt into a vest pocket. He collected my dish and chopsticks and beer can. He wiped each dish and chopstick, crushed each Bud can, rinsed a spill off the Kraft, collapsed the stove, capped the gas bottle and wrapped the whole of it in a cloth and returned the remains of our picnic to his rucksack. He stood. He brushed himself off. He adjusted the wrinkles in his waders. He collected his fly rod and looked past me with a frown upriver.

'Shall,' he said, 'we,' he said, 'continue?'

There are quiet moments for all of us, I suppose, when

experience turns us a few degrees one way or the other and what we see is new and sudden and alarming. Sato looked different to me as he fished ahead. He looked singular, calm, persistent, skilled, and distant. I could not grasp it, could not put words to the shame and confusion I felt as I stumbled behind him up that lovely, ruined river. Had I been discourteous? Had Sato been hurt? It seemed so – and after all, what place was it of mine to be so outraged by Japanese water? Yet how could Sato be un-conflicted? How could he live with the fly fishing aesthetic *and* the rampaging bulldozer, the pretty day *and* the puking night, and fail to be afflicted with the tension I felt so keenly? He was what? An assemblage of disconnected selves? In peaceful coexistence? So was this the trick to life? I had never wondered such a thing: *was there a trick to life? Was I missing it?* If this cozy knit of incongruities were Sato, then what was I? What could be said of this uncouth troll who slapped his way upstream, his brain-stem inflamed by contradiction, mad to seize the world and shake it?

That the world would not by my hands be shaken – this is what I discovered in the fell swoop of that clumsy afternoon. I felt the profound insufficiency of me. My language, my culture, my theories and my certainties, my clever slants and my bravado, my skill with a fly rod – these assets amounted, here and now, to a grasp on exactly nothing. Not only that – beyond that – I was afraid, and I had been afraid, I knew now, from the moment I stepped off the plane with my rod tube at Narita – no, from the moment back home when I had decided to venture forth and conquer, I thought, new lands and peoples and waters. I had been descending from there into a quiet, creeping terror since my neighbour had swept me off to the trout tank and afterward no listener had found my story the least bit outrageous or amusing or in any other way significant.

It would be years before the word *bewildered* would dawn on me – as in gone astray, led into the wild – but there I was, abruptly astray in the wilderness of my own existence. All afternoon, that fly rod felt useless, foolish, miscast in my hand – and I kept all language to myself.

When I hauled up on the bank beside Sato an hour from dusk I somehow, as if to compound my bewilderment, accepted a cigarette. I had caught nothing. I had seen no trout. I was numb and shivering. My back ached. My weary mind whirled through spheres of dizzy emptiness. That fishless river had beaten the crap out of me. I had waded nearly five kilometres. I had followed Sato over half a dozen dams. I had wet every fly in my box. I had understood nothing.

Sato, of course, had experienced mostly the same afternoon, except that now he looked peaceful as he smoked, possibly even content. At the sight of him, my shoulders slumped further and my mind lobbed a final hunk of bait. Sure. *It's not the catching, it's the fishing.* And off the hook wiggle the exploiters, the polluters, the near-sighted consumers, the ignorant farmers, the self-serving, make-work politicians – because who needs the actual trout anyway? Wasn't that nifty? Wasn't Japanese-style fly fishing just the perfect recreational bonsai, stunted but lovely, an ideal gimmick to deny the crisis of not a damn thing alive in the stream?

But this time I kept quiet. I was too tired, too cautious, too vacantly buzzed to speak. The web of concepts, beliefs, and opinions that I identified as 'me' was loosened and perilously a-tremble, like some new and unknown entity had blundered into the centre of it and was tearing out a hole.

'Shall we return?' asked Sato.

I couldn't wait.

We hiked out inside the mossy trough of a square-cornered concrete gutter that carried water down from that last high-mountain dam in a multi-kilometre feat of Rube Goldberg engineering that discharged, finally and pointlessly, into a terrace of long-abandoned rice paddies rimmed with the rusted garbage of bygone lives.

Wet boots scuffing, unrequited rods nodding, we switch-backed in silence down the darkening mountainside. Often in

Japan in those days, one would find in the middle of nowhere a vending machine that sold cold beer. And just so, at the edge of exhaustion, at the perimeter of a rock quarry beside a vacant sag shack, we hove into a colourful glow like a pair of light-starved moths. A guy would need a lot of alcohol to live this way, I found myself thinking as I spilled coins into the slot.

I bought too much beer, could hardly carry the cans. I drank too much, too fast, I drank while I walked, and I was loopy and out of breath when we at last reached the scene of that morning's trout fishing festival.

Fireworks popped in the sky from some other place in the village. I saw now beneath the multi-coloured glow that there were still pre-war thatched-straw roofs in this village, and above these persisted the wooden tower for the air-raid siren. Before us, too, the work of the bulldozer had been left to stand. Still the river swirled into that makeshift containment of its own stones. Still it trickled, scattered and diminished, out the downstream wall. The grill barrels smouldered. Trash festooned the riverbank. About the margins of the pond capered one old man, festively drunk and hoarsely loud, and one little boy in a state of jittery high excitement. The two were throwing firecrackers onto the pond. As we came closer we understood their reason: there was one trout left.

The trout held at mid-depth, a small dark mote finning faintly against the swirl of the current. 'Look! Look! There it is!' The old man staggered, thrusting a smouldering nub of cigarette toward the centre of the pool. 'Get it! Hit it! Ready, set – fire!'

The boy carried one of those pistol lighters. He shot flame across the fuse of a firecracker and flung the cracker in the direction of the fish. That explosion sent the trout darting every-which-way for thirty seconds or so before it settled uneasily once more in the wide-open of the pond.

'There it is! Look! Hit it!'

Bang!

This repeated until the old man saw us. Then the kid saw us. For a long few moments, they gaped in wonder at our exotic rods and fly fisher's raiment. Then slowly, inevitably, a new idea formed with such mutual certainty it was like watching a hand come down and draw cartoon dialogue above their heads.

'Please, mister, will you catch this fish for us, please?'

No way, I muttered and kept walking. Sato did not respond except to smile at the boy.

'Hey, you,' brayed the old man, 'you in the fancy pants. Can't you catch this fish? Huh?' He stumped toward us, his leathery face stretched around that ubiquitous gold-toothed farmer smile. 'Come here. Catch this fish for my grandson while I sit down and drink.'

'Please, mister? Please?'

'You fellas look like a couple of – '

That triggered Sato's gasping laugh. I asked him: What did the grandfather say?

'Space men,' he said. 'From space,' he said.

The kid threw another firecracker. *Bang!* 'Please?'

I said, 'No. Sorry.'

Sato stepped forward

'Don't,' I told him. I raised my arms, meaning to invoke the river, the day, the festival, my state of mind, all of it.

'It's okay,' Sato said.

'How is it okay?'

But he was moving. I groaned as he unhitched his fly. 'Come on. This isn't fishing.' But Sato ignored me and he climbed onto the dam rim. I retreated. I sat on a remaindered hump of rice-straw mulch at the edge of a cucumber field, snapped a beer and watched.

Which fly Sato tried first I couldn't say. He went to his knees and stayed low. He shot a long, soft cast – a decent meadow cast, unseen from the man all day – out beyond the trout and let the fly sink for ten or fifteen seconds. Then he slowly stripped it back. I could not see the trout, but I imagine it moved, because abruptly the old man shouted 'There it goes!' and the boy threw a firecracker. This outburst brought Sato up from his knees and precipitated discourse at a level of

Japanese that was deeply colloquial and well beyond my ear. But the boy dropped his firecrackers and shoved his hands in his pockets. The grandfather ejected some unbalanced hoarseness back at Sato and lit a cigarette.

Sato lit one too. Then he went back to work. He changed flies. He stalked low around the rim of the pond. This new fly he dropped with impressive skill onto the surface about one metre ahead of the trout's nose. He leaned, squinted, timed, then jerked the fly beneath the surface like he was fishing for television, enticing a big bonefish or a canny monster tarpon.

The beleaguered little hatchery trout darted away in fear of the fly – and then in fear of the grandfather, who resumed his yelling. The boy held fire, however, and once more Sato changed flies. To do this he sank down cross-legged on the pond rim in a posture that expressed a kind of serene stubbornness, an absolute determination to catch this fish. The boy moved in close to watch over Sato's shoulder. The grandfather brayed something in the general direction of the village. I understood this much: *last trout!*

I had the urge to charge forth, to stop this here and now, but by this passage I had also awakened to a squeamish interest in the event as spectacle, the way one feels when passing a car wreck. I stood then but approached slowly, feeling I was witness to a tragedy. Every interest, I felt, was bound to lose in this effort – the trout, the boy, the grandfather, Sato, myself, the river, the people of that village, and the people downstream of that village, and the people downstream of that time in the next generation. None of this was good, I believed, and yet as fireworks fizzled in the sky, no small number of villagers rushed forth between their straw-thatched houses, back to the pond to see this culminating excitement.

Last trout!
A stranger's going to catch it!
Look at that fantastic gear!
He's a fly fisherman!
He's going to catch the last trout!

As Sato changed flies a third time I felt a profound sense

of loneliness, what one feels, I suppose, when sliding into despair, or madness, into that irreversible dislocation of self when one's web of being is unstrung and nothing connects the way it had only moments before. Once Sato triumphed over that fish, once he and the rest were gratified, I faced a long, dark ride back to my apartment, and even then I would be farther from home than I ever planned to be – without friends, without water to fish, without the compass of my usual crusade.

I began to plunge then, falling into depths. My head spun. My pulse quickened. A prickly sweat erupted up my back and beneath my arms. I fought for air in that deepening darkness, sensing on some inchoate plane that this was so much more than it seemed to be, that this moment was the on-switch in the struggle between me and myself and that my true bewilderment had only just begun. I was here. Here was now. Yet I and here and now would never save one another. Nothing would ever be that simple. Only the deepest humility made sense – and therein was the struggle of a lifetime. Why ever had I thought otherwise?

I was still plunging when Sato finally put a hook in that dismal little fish. 'Oy!' erupted the grandfather. 'He's got it!'

'Pull it in!' shrieked the boy. 'Don't lose it!'

The rainbow shot around the pool in a panic. Sato held his rod dramatically high, as I imagined he was instructed by his master at the Tokyo casting pond. At some point while I was plunging, Sato had started another cigarette, and now, having stabilized the situation, he began to puff away while playing the trout one-handed around the pool. A single time it jumped, wriggled desperately in the firework-tinged dusk light, then splatted back down, still hooked. Throughout this, Sato's face displayed an enigmatic smile, like a man in the throes of some faint and private ecstasy. Meanwhile the boy and his grandfather charged around the dam rim from opposite directions, closing on Sato, imploring him to succeed and hollering toward the gathering crowd. 'He's got it! Come on! He's caught the fish! Come and look!'

Indeed by now an audience of maybe twenty villagers had drawn close to the pond. They chattered and kibitzed while Sato worked the tiny trout like it was a ten-pound Rogue River steelhead. He let it run, brought it back to heel, let it run again, followed its surges along the dam rim with the boy and the old man yipping behind. Through all this drama, Sato kept to his prim and silent joy, said nothing to anyone, answered no one's demands, stubbornly followed not one whit of the various and urgent advisories hurled across the pond.

'Oy!' yelled the flustered grandfather. 'Look at this. Look. The fancy man has hooked grandson's fish. What do you make of that?'

'Give it to me!' pleaded the boy. 'Pull it in! I'm going to hit it with a rock!'

Only when Sato had finished his cigarette and tucked the filter into his vest pocket did he move to conclude the deal.

I was sweating freely now, just about embolic with fear for my time ahead, and so I will never forget those next few moments.

That little trout was exhausted. Sato eased it toward him beneath the surface of the pond. As it arrived, he wet his hands as not to disturb its envelop of slime. He slid a palm beneath the fish, cradled it and turned it upside down. The trout hung there, still as death, while Sato set down his rod. Voices rose, admiring the pale, hatchery-fat belly. I could tell that Sato had used a barbless hook when he simply ticked the fly with a fingertip and released the trout's jaw.

Now came the grasping hands, the excited words. 'Oy. You. See here. That's my grandson's trout.'

'Thank you! Thank you! Give it! Give it!'

'Fantastic, isn't it? All that equipment? To catch one little fish?'

'But he caught it. When no one else could.'

'Give it, mister, please, I'm going to smash it with a rock.'

'Oy. Grandson. Take the trout.'

Sato appeared to hear none of this. He stood, elevating the

trout just clear of the boy's swiping hands. He turned one-eighty on the rim of the dam. In three or four kicks with his wader boots, he rooted out a spillway. Water poured out the back of the dam. Before I could grasp what was happening – in the instant before I understood that 'pupil' and 'master' were in the best sense interchangeable; before I knew that I had fallen into deep water, sure, but I would call for a hand and Sato's would appear; before I saw that Sato had made his outlaw spurs that day just as I had touched wisdom; and just as the cries of disbelief and protest and outrage arose – that last small trout was out the back of the dam, kinking madly down the spillway on its perfect way into the flow, to freedom.

Sato showed no defiance or rancour. He responded to no insult or charge. He reeled up and tidied out the irregularities in his exotic attire. He nipped off his fly and dropped it into the palm of the bewildered, disconsolate boy. He waved away invective from the old man like gnats from his face. He came down off the dam and when he reached me his pace was unhurried but eyes were alive and he was grinning like a mud-mad river troll.

'I think,' he said, 'that we,' he said, 'should go,' he said, 'now.'

Colin Higgins

I was born in Nottingham in 1958. Idylls were at a premium but a neighbour gave me a copy of *Mr Crabtree Goes Fishing* which looked like a glimpse of one. I tore it up in a rage a few years later; I forget why, as I read it every day. A gang of children regularly fished the Trent, and despite the early hardware we learned to fish.

Angling was a perfect focus for kids like us – but teachers thought otherwise and the steady drip of endorsed ridicule made it a secret vice. Or was I just obsessed? Certainly there was no elegant applause for knowing the weight of the record rod-caught lobster. Something was up, because by seventeen I wanted nothing to do with myself. Jobs meant darkroom technician, layout artist, film lecturer, importer of hand-made goods, film actor, property developer, whatever spared me enough to time to paint, fish and write – which I try to do full-time these days.

Back Waters

When my fishing mate's family hauled his sorry arse off to the other side of the world as one of the last ten-pound poms, angling took a backseat. We'd had a good run, thrashing Hi-Los across municipal ponds until the most moribund jack gave chase, or turning the river into a froth of badly aimed coffin leads. But at seventeen even I, a boy whose tactics were informed by the golly gosh of *Mr. Cherry Goes Fishing with Jim and Tim*, was looking for more.

Jamie's disappearance to Sydney was a full stop in a paragraph already looking for an ending. His hair was growing horizontally in a gravity-defying feat of prog rock mimesis, while mine was becoming unfashionably short, as rhythm and blues provided the template for what I liked to think of as my style – a vision admittedly more Trent towpath than Mississippi Delta. On our last outing he caught a perch on a jointed plug intended for a legendary pike, a fish bigger than most of our *esox*, with his first cast. It even impressed the bailiff, who swore colourfully when he saw it. The first time he'd out-fished me and I was pleased, a neat farewell to childhood and a promise of better things to come. Or so you would have thought. My father had taken me fishing first. Not an angler, the waterside was his release from the clack of knitting machines and twelve-hour mill shifts and he encouraged my enthusiasm, accompanying me on trips and happy to supply the weekly copy of *Angling Times* instead of *The Victor*. When he had a massive heart attack as I entered my teens, Dad returned from intensive care a demi-ghost, wearing the look of a man who'd seen wider shores than our park lake. Jamie had been the right boy in the right place with the wrong rod, but now he was on his way out too. The land of Boney and Skippy was a world apart then and I wondered what it would make of my hippy mate. It would be some time till I next cast a line.

Not that fish ever left the picture. Getting a place at a London art college, waterside drawing trips became an opportunity to ponder aquatic life as much as (well, considerably more so than) personal investigations of the wider world and I became anchored in juvenile certainties of angling and art. The muddy churn of the Thames continued without my questioning hook, likewise the local canal, with my painting similarly retarded. Without noticing, roach poles became poles, swim feeders just feeders – and never hair rollers – and keep nets a fine mesh rather than the gudgeon-strangling webs we'd employed, if they were used at all. Art school didn't valorise my stolid draughtsmanship in a way I'd hoped and I hadn't the discipline or social ease to develop. I was stuck between worlds, the insecure working-class product of a Grammar School, and a cloak of cynicism kept out the prying and the helpful alike. You could keep the future: I was having nothing to do with it.

Five years on, the future was getting on fine without me. A long-term relationship had faltered and a short one had gone belly-up too. Even I could see the threads of past failures were strangling me like the fish in my three-foot Efgeeco, but what to do? Where had it all gone wrong? There was always angling. The suture of old and new, hope and despair could take place on a river bank if it could happen anywhere. Clearly, art school had left a mark, even if it was just psycho-bollocks and a college job teaching.

The childhood kit had disappeared some years before, flogged for the price of a night in the pub on a flea market. Shopping for new stuff wasn't without peril, but while the terminology had changed and the smell of varnish and maggots was no more, there was enough familiarity that it felt like coming – if not home, then at least getting the right turn-off on the mind motorway (the seventies still clung to my thought patterns, as they do now). True, there weren't cased fish in their deathly idylls behind the counter and most of the stuff was from the far east and made of carbon, but it was a tackle shop and I left it a ton lighter with the sketchy basics of a kit. I may have been three parts toss-pot as my ex insisted, but as a queue of chub succumbed to the dipping waggler, the remaining segment was still unreconstructed fisherman. While the light faded on that first returning day, a perch as big as the last one I'd seen came into the net, a nice symmetry and one I could invest meaning in. The world may still be mad but at least I had my divining rod back and it seemed to work.

Crystal Tips

Canals. Guaranteed to divide opinion. Aquatic skip or urban lung? Featureless drain or charming linear fishery? We had one at the top of the street where I grew up. I can just remember it as an overgrown, iridescent swamp through which pioneering chaps with beards and Breton caps skippered The Sandpiper or Lazy Daze, navigating round dead lurchers on BSA Bantams. I suppose they were the watery equivalent of the railway preservationists, desperate to hold on to past wonders while everyone else was happy to see them filled in. If they thought about them at all between *Take Your Pick* and *Sunday Night at the London Palladium*. Given that our particular waterway was a convenient overflow for the dye works and host to whatever heavy metals the foundries chose to dispense, it was small wonder fishing forays were rare and wholly unsuccessful. If you looked closely you could sometimes see a stickleback – that last redoubt of nature in the toxic stew an arse-end of industrialisation had left by way of inheritance – gills pumping, spines bristling, inviting all comers to have a go if they think they're hard enough – but it was generally acknowledged that the canal was entirely lifeless below the plimsoll line. It was, as canals often still are, a sort of crime scene.

A few years later British Waterways re-instituted the banks, dredged the channel and generally tidied things up, but the industry was still there, probably on short time and definitely using machinery Arkwright and Brunel would have felt at home with. The only way I could conceive of fishing it was with the tiniest of crow quills and a single maggot or sliver of flake. There were bites, certainly; the float bobbed now and again, but nothing with the wit or will to drag it under;

doubtless the same stickleback wary in case the bread was a morsel of arsenic-bleached rag.

It was only as a young adult that I saw the same waterway giving up bags of fat-backed roach, but that was during my Sabbatical in the Wilderness and I watched with fascination as other anglers prised impossibly healthy fish from the hitherto slough. Its proximity to home heightened my disbelief, much as a time traveller might marvel that his corner shop was now a Waitrose.

I've never seen myself with a pole and elastic, mainly for reasons of snobbery but also because I can't be bothered with all the gear. When I fish canals it's with a rod and reel, using tactics not far removed from my childhood. So it was thus I found myself on board a narrowboat with my girlfriend's family, 13ft of ringed carbon and a small tackle bag. Now it doesn't need a Jonathan Cainer (or Evadne Price for the oldies: 'think lucky and you'll be lucky') to foresee that an extended family group, each of whom one's connection with is tentative, in a space that would have the RSPCA invoking legislation, is not to be entertained lightly. But entertain it I had to if I was to keep peace with the object of my affection. It was early days in our love-in and I was keen to make an impression. The rod was my get-out clause, an excuse to wander up the bank when cutlery stood in for switchblades or the confines were used to air ancient enmities in which I had no part.

The Shropshire Union is about as far from the crack dens synonymous with city canals as it is possible to imagine. If it isn't, do not disabuse me. While I had the kit to fish the far bank should I need to, the towpath was quiet enough to try close in, and that was to be my first option, to which end I'd brought a collection of crystal wagglers. Now I have mixed feelings about these floats. On the one hand they were conceived with skittish fish in mind, roach so frightened of their own shadow that one cannot think they eat at all, but hang about in groups like trick-or-treaters, pulling the door bell and always assuming it's the Addams Family on the other end. On the other hand I know enough about optics to conclude that, in the wrong circumstances, the clear plastic tube would operate like one of those glass portholes property developers put in dingy lofts, illuminating the watery world like a searchlight and scattering my quarry from Tipton to Llandudno. Still, needs must, and as the girls began their debate about what happened to Barbie's hair in 1974 or who Nigel Proudfoot touched up after the sixth-form disco or whatever nonsense daughters choose to torture one another with, I made my excuses and strode out of earshot.

It was so quiet, casting seemed like rustling a bag of chips and bits in evensong. I aimed for the near drop-off about twenty feet along. The float plopped in a way only locked-off wagglers can – that is to say with the maximum possible disturbance – folded, hunched, then rose to reveal the tiny red insert. Thirty seconds passed, I fed minimally, then got a take. A nice red-fin of about half a pound. A minute later, same routine, another roach a little smaller. This continued for the next half hour, and as the girls moved barely audibly to Why Grandma Never Liked You, You Bitch, the fish kept coming, nothing bigger than 14oz but good sport all the same. Then the swim swelled a few inches, drowning the float tip and signalling that another boat was coming round the corner. As it did the engine shut off. Bugger, they were going to moor up in my swim for the night. Narrow-boaters fit neatly into a few distinct categories: retired couples in rude good health with tinted glasses who I imagine to be equally enthusiastic doggers; students in hire boats who want to get sunburnt, laid and pissed by turns; and families like ours on holiday, a social experiment of a most ill-advised kind. The newcomers fitted none of these taxonomies but as they moored up I saw they had a kind of glow about them, a fairness of flesh, a youth and vigour rarely seen, even in Shropshire.

'Hi there, how you doing?' said the eldest.

They were American.

I nodded in the way Brits do, half way between obsequiousness and inner rage. They hadn't tied up in what I'd come to view as my personal riparian fiefdom, but their noise was enough for me to change the rig to something suitable for the far shelf. I looked now and again at their vessel, not wanting to stare but seeing that it fit none of the flowerpots and castles or quasi-industrial bargee fantasies I'd come to expect. It was bright, but not in a good way, rather like folk singers in pubs wear bright jumpers to hide a miserable streak a mile wide.

The float slid away, the two-and-a-half-pound line went taut, and the clutch slipped to the steady pump, pump, pump of a big bream. I've always liked bream, especially large ones. They have a nobility about them and behave as Margaret Rutherford might, if woken suddenly from an afternoon nap in *A Passport to Pimlico*: with astonishment but impeccable manners. It pretty much filled the landing net, and as I turned round casually as fishermen do to see if anyone had noticed, pretending enormous fish were entirely to be expected when I was around and didn't I land it neatly while you're gawping – I saw two of the yanks were. Staring, that is.

'Nice fish', one said.

He looked surprised that their medium of conveyance held anything of the sort and I wanted to tell him about the large carp I'd seen cruising (and which I was unequipped to land) but felt he might be from the banks of the Colorado or somewhere used to larger species so I nodded again. Ambiguous nodding I can do; spoken language is where it all goes wrong. The eldest American edged nearer. Our own boat had gone quiet now, the sisters having slaughtered each other in a Jacobean grimoire, become sated with psychological sniping or – in a parallel universe – having agreed to differ and broken out the Abba Top Trumps.

The American told me his name. It was Brad or Clint or something, and he began to engage me in conversation. Good manners are all very well in Ealing comedies, but will be my undoing. Instead of suggesting he feck off, I found myself agreeing it was indeed a still evening, the countryside was especially beautiful, we were blessed with the weather and so on, while a formless weight of expectation began to rest upon my shoulders from some unknown but terrible source. I cast about me for a significant clue from this Richie Cunningham look-alike and his chum, but beyond unnaturally good teeth could find nothing to support my anxiety. Other anglers will well know the attraction water has for the suicidal, psychotic, drunk and those released prematurely back into the community, and will have an armoury of responses and sometimes weaponry, but this was something other and I chided myself for my cynicism.

Then came his coup de grace.

'Do you know The Lord?'

I wanted to throw *non-sequiturs* about Lord Bradford's water ending some miles back, did he mean Lord Sutch, and gags about the Upper House, but we were so far beyond the irony curtain that it would have been wasted. Don't get me wrong, I'm not against a bit of religion, Old Timey or otherwise, but this looked like a binary, right/wrong, heaven/hell evangelism with no room for quips outside the devil's own parlour. How could I not have noticed? The rainbow on the boat, the chorus that was now wafting over the levels, the clean limbs and bright eyes unsullied by Tim Taylor's Landlord and the music of Robert Johnson? Perhaps I should have made shrill Richard Dawkins noises or rolled my eyes Linda Blair-style as in *The Exorcist,* but he was too far gone for fripperies. I don't remember exactly what I said, but it was something about scaring the fish – which he had, possibly with his teeth, and I tried to work out which was worse: the antis who love fish as our equals, or the pastor for whom fish didn't even register, apart from in parable form.

Our boat, when I arrived back, was quiet, and once I'd cut a hole in the atmosphere I found a space in my bunk.

'What was all that about?' I said to the woman who is now my wife.

'That? Oh, we were just talking. We're fine.'

I lay awake wondering how efficient a canal boat was as a tool for biblical conversion in rural Britain, and what sort of people would choose it – but, unable to square the circle and making sure my filleting knife was within reach, drifted off to dream of slabs who wore tweed and pulled see-through floats in Salopian cuttings.

Float

Blank: void of incident or result, puzzled, nonplussed, having no knowledge or understanding.

A ripple etches the pond.

The sun has disappeared behind a white billow and my float pulls its anchor. Leaves show their pale bottom with a long shush, thunder half an hour away. Only the tip, red and daunted as the tail lamp on a missed train, loiters in open water. There are no lilies, no drift weed. No finger of land to crack the black mirror, two realms, the perch and mine.

So it's a flask of tea and two Rockys. Not one for portable music, I think of a tune and break a biscuit to *Jolene*. Dolly's battle with the redhead reaches its climax, then Amy Winehouse goes into *Rehab*. Tea is drunk strong, the stuff of bad news and missing fish. A red-hot tip of another kind has sent me here, fine lines smashed and matchmen sent home grumpy. The solitary fish of records, top of the pyramid, heart-breaker, fool-maker.

Silence descends. Ancient churches and ponds give off a quiet. It has a smell and a colour, the synaesthesia of complete absence. I don't like this place. I scatter a few maggots in the direction of the float but they're grapeshot, wide and ineffectual. There are some big roach in here, two-pounders. Photographed one almost that weight with a missing top lip. Ran out of film when the next one came out bigger. A likely story – late on the barricades of the digital revolution, me. Another old snap, out of focus in fading light. The keepnet has a striped Godzilla centre-stage, the chub dwarfed onlookers, the Daniel Lambert of perch filling the hoop but not here and not now. I want to pack up but don't like the quarter mile to the lane, a hemmed *V* of sycamore set with ruined houses, though how anyone could have endured such a benighted gully is anyone's guess. There were other ponds in the cutting but they're choked with reedmace now, more vestiges, even the bailiff wanted shut of the job and his visits were few and far between.

I wind in, enough's enough.

Bass Relief

You couldn't move for decent sorts, dreadlocked white boys taking their expensive vowels and rescue mongrels and fragrant local talent for a walk. I'd have finished up snaring a Staffordshire-Collie cross called Iolanthe on the backcast and pitching it into the Atlantic. Or showing off and putting a 4-oz bomb in my forehead. Three Special Brewed locals with NASA launching Penns crowded in the right corner nudging the third breaker but I looked enough of a grockle without an Enter the Dragon bitchcaster.

Landlubbers keep their dog-snagging gear for the ocean – ten squid Chinese rods with erectile dysfunction, pink mono, comedy hooks, random feathers, baits pulped into handy geometric shapes. Sand eels and prawn butties swapped DNA in the car foot-well, mayonnaise as social lubricant. With the inverted snobbery of a tight-arse, I took my leave.

Along the coast in the shadow of Knocker's Wheal were bass. The climb down from the engine house was grim; steep and slippery enough without getting my Shining Emperor jammed or negotiating the burnt-out car. The thought of being Gathered to God for dislodging a joy-ridden Renault wasn't inviting. An indecent swell had me casting chug bugs from a granite boulder, waves lapping my Vans (footwear choice for the soul boy of middle years) or sucking shingle twenty feet below, mug fishing; a siren call, the kind of thing that has pork butchers manning the lifeboat. The kind of thing that has reporters in court shoes on south-west TV nodding wryly while the wind scatters their lowlights outside the coroner's. The kind of thing that scares me shitless. I do fear proper nice when my trainers get gulf-streamed. A disinterested tackle shop owner scooped a few thousand *hyperoplus* that had escaped becoming industrial fertiliser into a tank as I chatted to no-one about bass rigs next day, but shook his head when I described the jolly.

'Never go to Tubby's point,' he barked before swapping a futures dealer's Bolly ration for a shark pole. It got an O'Shaughnessy in me. One failure leads to another and the cupboard door falls open. Every slight and knock, each mis-chosen word, enemies real and imagined, wave from a stage revolve. The high-jump bar of a minus sign halts positive leaps for the evening. I was a one-man angry brigade.

A man can have strange dreams under a twelve-person tent when there are only three and the portaloo is leaking formaldehyde fumes. My stateless pleasure dome decreed a stock-take: places, people wise and foolish.

John made his own reels; you sensed tragedy but he could have been a machinist at Royce. It was piece-work charving Brenda or trotting for dace. The Trent might turn to molten gold at 4 o'clock but he wouldn't let on. A Sphinx on a wicker stump.

He used the longest quills we'd ever seen and shirt-button leading.

Where is he now? Where is *Chest Wader?* Edward Smith stood in Titanic heads of foam imperious among the turds and bubbles mending his line, feeding, re-baiting, just a head and shoulders at the outfall. Even his keepnet barely broke surface. Chub would enter like the stillborn, hardly knowing what had befallen them. Perhaps he fell without the river at his back?

The boy whose mouth we filled with sand. A lovely boy who laughed at everything so we topped him up like bastards; where's he? He only laughed because he didn't know how not to, his mother shaking sand out for a week. Heathens when the swim went dead.

The man who fished the slider; he was good. A don among miners letting me look in his basket. Linnaean graded floats, shot, weights in divine order, a magus. He knew how to fish. Fat blokes with a fag clenched in a toothless gob, they knew how. Touch legering a cord of platil where the canal met the river, ember signals in pus lips at dusk.

Barbel lads on the tidal stretch with bowed braid and waste-bin feeders. They didn't know how to fish but they knew how to love. Towpath Heffners in a Calorgas glow with a queue of semi-virgins; cheesecloth good girls lead halfway to the Humber.

The rheumy-eyed carrion at the tackle shop counter neither did they know. Judging the customers, duff St. Peters but for a tip they'd race to a piss puddle.

The man who conjured tench from the perch pond knew. The man who caught nothing knew. Mister Varnish and the plywood box knew. The silent man with all the 30s knew something.

A kind man knew and the teacher with the wizard.

A fresh Cornish wind blew in scattering doubts on an occluded front.

Days

Some times are garlanded in light, abuzz with the hive unconscious; other times are owl pellet: dislocated bones, feather-sick and midnight bile.

This was all sunlit. We put in at first quiet, bows slapping like a fairground fat lady in an aluminium swimsuit, stomach knots and bleary. October burnt off river wraiths who rose to judgement, a Believer went over the side where it burrowed out of sight against the flow. The platypus kissed the silt then I wound back two turns. D lobbed his Grandma in and both rods shook. A seven-pounder came aboard curling its Popeye lip. I changed to a lazy spoon on the 18ft line and took a 5lb fish and we went upriver, finding pike.

Better men, better fisherman will unpick a stream. I lack the guile or the perseverance, rivers wash over me, taken in by the wide-screen view I miss the sub-plot. Not today. A king-fisher bobs for fry, an in-out Bioscope joke our grandfathers enjoyed before they left their Saturday squeeze for foreign parts. A heron stiff as garden-centre plaster watched, and a military *V* of geese. Coots and mallard fled then settled in our wake, cat-calling.

The poorest company on-board, me; a bad marriage has fewer words.
> yep,
> nah,
> is it?
> in't it?

I'm a gonner with a rod. Sky-eyed. Quieter than Billy No Mates's straight man. A zombie with a bucket of gormless mock-perch, inscrutable dollies both. What was there to say? Double figures and the sun barely over the willows. By way of a rest we took out the bait rods. Herring tails went in and D's lamprey sat in a cloud of gore, floats as perky as ballerina tits by the posh moorings. I'll stare all day watching how they draw the surroundings in, become a negative, a positive space, float as gas giant, red dwarf, black hole, migraine float, hope float, float as universal despair. D was impatient to be among the fish and it was his boat. The Honda farted and we were away into more pike, bigger now. I had a 16 long as a snake as the river narrowed but conclusively trumped; out of a hole he plucked a 27. We cut the engine and pulled about, first an olive flank big, bigger, then a clutching dive, then a head of watchful eyes, a big girl filling the lure net lean as anything. A 30 after Christmas no worries, unmarked.
> Pictures,
> into a bag.

She swam away. We turned back and sun dogs followed us along the right bank with frost.

Another day on the sorceress. I have a plastic coracle that's carried like a hat. Not fit for rivers, I wear it nonetheless.

This day I drifted in my bonnet throwing spinners and plugs at a place where the current turns a circle, eventually. Mostly you're suspended midstream between two wide sandy banks. I like the ride. It was flat still with a grey sky, the water no more than a half-tone darker. Two people chatted clear as day ten minutes' walk along the bank; there was a hunting horn somewhere; a man with a cocked gun and a spaniel nodded: a tablemat bucolic, fishing unplugged. I knew there was a run of sea trout twenty feet below and hoped the pike might notice. The quiet, thick as ear wax truly, a nervous quiet into which went a sewin spoon. A river can change on a heartbeat. She went jittery. Tidal, pre-monsteral, a moon thing. Spots of rain, then nothing, a different nothing.

I counted the spoon down some more but it came back drunk with twigs barely enough tow to turn the swivel. Deeper, thirty feet and more, among dead trees and dead men's dug-out canoes, primal fishing without a word of fancy – then a take. Spoons are bad hookers so I pulled hard and an irritable jack came up, then panicked. The big bitch that grabbed my mate's 17 was holed up watching, I just knew.

Luck be a Lady

Black Crow was a feral pigeon that hung out on the ridge tiles of the houses opposite.

'Black crow is watching you,' Mam would say when I started to play up. Sometimes a row of birds looked down silhouetted against the skyline cocking their heads, counting my errors from the next street. It's an alarming prospect to be judged by the avian kingdom and found wanting, aged three.

'I saw a thunderbolt drop out the sky, kill a horse and set fire to a barn,' she told me later, turning the mirrors to face the wall and putting the cutlery away at the first peal of thunder. This animist landscape fit comfortably with her Catholicism and I wasn't able to unpick the two threads – martyrs, imps, charms, sacred medallions, portentous pigeons woven seamlessly – with either likely to influence the football pool results. While Kent Walton commentated on the Jackie Pallo - Mick McManus grapple from a crumbling town hall lined with abusive dowagers, the scores flicked up and Saint Jude and Joan the Wad* wrestled for eight score draws. Both were unreliable benefactors.

'Have a good week, till next week' was the way things always ended. Like Kent's accent or the park lake skimmers, belief was a hybrid.

For all my faith in a rising barometer and the value of a well-placed PVA bundle, my Polaroids are still clouded by the view through the net curtains of No. 17. I wouldn't call myself unusually credulous, but the elements still have prophetic status wrapped in scientific augury. The lunar cycle is one factor that has insinuated itself into a relativistic doctrine. My inner rationalist, an enlightenment cove with a bell jar and a dead mouse, insists the moon is too remote to exert influence on rivers and ponds. On the other temporal lobe, the shamanic Me quivers with those aquatic organisms who hail the waxing deity – tentacles flailing, mouths gaping, whips thrashing towards a celestial Betty Page in a parthenogenetic orgy. It's impossible to say if bugs rattle the chain that turns on higher species but perhaps they do and the notion is agreeable: a kind of string theory with peanuts and boilies.

Dead baits tickle my auspices too: not as committed to a joey mackerel as one chap who lured five large pike with a single mummified example, going to desperate lengths to retrieve the lucky fish (if expiring on a factory ship in the Baring Straits, being freeze-dried, shrink-wrapped, posted and dangled on a pair of trebles can be considered fortunate). I have been known to pare catching trout into ever smaller parts, presenting them as slivers on a size 8 before giving up the ghost. Why do I do that? Maybe the transmigration of salmonid soul through jack bait swells the pike's ego and he turns head-hunter. Maybe there's a saline-freshwater food interdiction Grandmother Pike likes to flout. Maybe dead baits attain posthumous ennoblement through the power of their allure. Maybe I'm full of shit. Can you hear me, Mother? On the one hand, on the other. Jesus, they were pigeons and they didn't care and neither do fish. They swim, they eat, they make baby fish. I'll hold on to that.

I've never ascribed the same daemonic properties or fancy talk to rods: perhaps because bad days follow good with the same wand, or more likely I'm just proletarian when it comes to gear. Angling's own brands, fishing's chicken dipper, tackle's tea-rose in a vac-formed wishing well do for me, sure in the knowledge that a nice bit of cane and silk trim would turn my head and I'd be trading the children's Ninky Nonk for an agate standoff ring in a Faustian auction. Sometimes, when I catch people sniggering at my alarms, held together by carpet tape and a crust of lithium like a depressed roadie doing his final sound check, I want for better things – but I know my place in the pantheon. It's with Outsiders, not Olympians. It works, it is sufficient, and maybe all that varnish is a sin when there are people starving. There were no Barders on Galilee, as my mother never said.

The same isn't true of the terminal end, the bits that matter. They're subject to all manner of ritual knotting and twisting where any diversion from best practice sees the process abandoned and restarted. Not everything is subject to presentiment or the denial of plain facts; some stuff has to be worked through and tested. Lures considered the embodiment of vulgarity on one water, gold-spangled arse-wagglers with a split rubber skirt find favour where puritanical glide baits don't: hot milf or repressed bluestocking, experiment pays. But only to a point. That point is that angling, like Littlewoods' pools or TV wrestling, had at least an apparent outcome and offered a few rules the house didn't – the place boiled constantly from a lack of wherewithal and undiagnosed mental ill-health. Dénouements were rare – never complain, never explain. The mad-bad-sad tendency of a brother who found a useful foil in my unformed personality was one example; that equation needs Babbage's indifference engine, a mechanical brain of dispassionate interlocking beams to do the sums and find where error lies, starting with a minus-22-year age difference. On the plus setting it was his old catalogues that set me on the fishing trail – probably before they were snatched back as bargaining chips in some emotional attrition – but there are at least two sides to every story. Those were the days before every psychiatric nuance had a definition and a handy title to be mulled over on *Woman's Hour*. Now the malaise would be a double-barrelled syndrome with a range of medication, a support group and a High-Street charity shop; then it was a case of lie low when his safety valve spluttered or head down to the river bank. The upside of this lack of closure, emotional and existential, is a capacity to juggle limitless possibilities that would blunt Occam's razor on its first stubbly pass. Fishing is the perfect vehicle for pondering infinite hypotheses; winsomely anthropomorphic, rigorously scientific, remorselessly self-critical but majoring on the balancing act that throws up notions like fractals. Insanities, inanities, temporary consciousness in an uncaring universe or Dame Nature, Gaia and St. Non flattered by a mole hill and wasp grub offering?

Carp have always been the focus of the confused, the blank canvas, the face of Garbo on which to write dreams. Anglers outgun them like Rambo putting a hook in every morsel, or out-think them, regarding the fish as a Lewis chessman, thick-set, bog-eyed and moving to antique endgames. Roach fill the gap for me. They appear in a swim like ghosts. Big ones can bust your brain. I remember an afternoon on a pond taking small carp and decent perch before a few huge roach moved in with a shoal – keeping them relied on feed, five maggots or six, where they wanted them and when. Half an hour later they were boiling like pet Koi, piggy-backing up the line. Then the flick of a rod can kill a swim for hours and you're wondering whether to dim your bale arm with magic marker or pull out your teeth.

That's where we get our reputation for misanthropy. We think we've got it cracked, then a single oak leaf falling·on the water becomes the synecdoche for winter and they're gone, vanished to insignificance which is more than invisible. It's a minus, it's the domino-tumbling record ruined by a bluebottle. So we start all over again on a different tack, or work back from the oak leaf down endless dead-ends until we arrive at nothing.

*Joan the Wad was a pixie charm sold in the back of Sunday tabloids.

Goodbye Mister Chippie

We kissed until we couldn't, until our faces were sucked into anaesthesia. The Mobylette knew its way through lowing herds and night mists to the bus stop at the edge of the village, the one on the route that came four times a day, an occasional red comet pausing at farmers' pubs and grassy triangles that were somewhere once, leaving its diesel and fag smoke-tail. Then we kissed some more until we looked like stroke victims in our big coats and went for some scampi from her mum's deep-freeze.

She photographed like a model. There's only one picture and she's a bling angel, a retro-lux perfume advertisement. In regular life she was mousey and myopic, casual and funny and clever as a cat.

I'd look at the timetable as we came up for air, the wondrous schedule that gave sanctuary at its limited request stop, and I'd see dead flies who'd made their way behind the glass as maggots, and withered without feeling a breeze on their wings or Alsatian shit on their feet, and marvel at mortality; but I mostly thought squats – roach bait of choice – and returned for industrial petting.

Riding back, 12.3 miles on the clock, the stroker labouring

over the canal bridge with a whine like those dying musca, I was in crisis.

Two months before I couldn't wait to get to the damp patch and slide the rod out of its bag, thread the line through the rings, put the float, shot and hook on. Bait it like a sacrament, scatter peace offerings and settle to ritual communion with cold water. Yet now it seemed distant.

The pursuit had been replaced by an ache; I'd chased the park roach only to discover a Palladio behind the wall and a lake stuffed with glittering mirrors – and I'd been handed the key. A golden key that changed the stars in their tracks. The key from *Take Your Pick*.

Losing it wasn't instant but it was inevitable. At 17 I was mostly jacket and the remaining bits were tackle. Apart from a knowledge of freshwater fish and the means to allure them there was nobody at home – and she was no fish. We couldn't tremble knees at public transport outposts indefinitely. I had to choose, to trade one obsession for another. Simple.

My bait was rudimentary. Her brother was reading philosophy so I devoured Wittgenstein, John Stewart Mill and Plato in the hope of impressing, choking on the ideas. Got a holiday job operating a lathe badly and charmed her lovely wise mother with the seriousness of my serious intent. I became ridiculous by degrees.

Then one day we came back to mine. Past the bins, through the dripping laundry, beneath the kitchen window with the Co-op number and in the back door. You had to feel sorry for her. This was the kind of place men at the centre lived in, the men nice girls volunteered to serve tea and cake to, men in the final stages of cirrhosis or broken dreams, the ones too near death for an up-skirt lunge. Not the house of a boy doing A levels. Not the home of a boy at all.

You could see it in the line of her mouth and the set of her lovely shoulders. I tried to distract her, talking quicker than Michael Miles in the Yes-No interlude. Don't look there, look over here, look at me where everything's still okay. Where the ashtrays don't overflow and there's no half-full piss bucket on the stairs. You sensed the contagion next time we kissed – I was getting too heavy. Heavy? I was exhausted. There'd been AAA shot in my heart since we met. Now stupid Cupid was down to crow quills.

Then one day the gong sounded and I pedalled my Mobylette into life like Monsieur Hulot, never to return. I went back once just to feel what it was like before the lights all went out, to the bus stop with the flies and empty-eyed moths staring at the gaps, but a replacement service wouldn't take long. The keeper had slipped the dogs and seen me off with pleasantness. There were to be no golden Leneys and the door in the wall was bricked up with good wishes.

I parked the bike between the bins and the bog, climbed the stairs to the attic, got out my Crabtree and tore it into ten thousand pieces, making the silent heaves of someone enlightened too quickly: the tablecloth trick that didn't quite work, an Axminster rug pulled away sudden.

The little Mitchell came out of its box and the handle was turned like always to watch the spool go in and out; it was all that was ever going in or out.

Her father once talked about fishing so I winged it with a tale about Blue Duns and this stream I knew but I was coarse and now we all knew it. The game girl knew most of all.

Then the pregnant cork perchers with their gloss varnish and pointless spiral whipping were laid out, from the days before Young Mister Grace got the time-and-motion men in and dispensed with silk trim. The Avons, the sticks and the Billy Lane Missile I hated too; even the big rod from three Christmases before was ridiculous. So I set about dismantling myself like the three-piece until there was nothing left but hollowness and glass and the open bait dropper of esteem.

It wasn't my mate going to Australia that made me pack it

in, it was them. How could I have buried that? The patrician line who knew the cut of my jib and wanted to spring me or paint me into a corner. Or watch me like the flies behind the glass, listening to the buzz and seeing the final kicks. How did I not remember?

The unquiet pitch thirty-three years on. December didn't used to be this hard. Venables' inky spate with the man and boy striking into a vortex, tilted like a Russian film looking as though they'd hooked the river itself, dragging the frame off the deficient page. Truth is it's fruitless, you can fill her with worms or troll a lure all a pale day and catch no more than ennui.

The Trent has always been the trespasser, stealing into fields to pluck a sheep from damp pasture, filling cellars and football pitches, beguiling and claiming. Daughter of an antique flow that left the Welsh mountains and coursed east, she has the wandering tendency now, undecided and shallow, impulsive and treacherous.

An eddy opens, a watery chrysanthemum: flood flowers. Bouquets from an unsuspected blackthorn tricked from its bank by snow melt until the caved roots unpicked themselves. Fish perch not fat robins, no song except the remorseless river plucking stolen branches. This is low country, never go back country, the land of lost content.

Someone said something unkind and true and I needed to walk it out where kindness and unkindness started.

Starlings drew question marks.

Ruby glyphs in afternoon contrails, letters in the sky. They'd sent me here, with their intimations; sometimes you have to walk and sometimes you have to fish the scoured river.

Cooling towers pass left and right as she turns again, super-annuated rooks making square moves, wandering the back scene. I'd seen him first as a smudge, a life-shape while the tow path unwound; not many people stand to fish any more: ours is an era of trappers, not stalkers.

Accommodations are reached on the bank, a confederation of
minds put solidity to one side; people on the edge hail strangers.
He'd strewn margarine tubs with hemp and casters and red
maggots; Golden Spread labels couldn't conceal the swarming
unconsidered life. There was no accommodation here. This
was not a man who cared for the passage of bodies one way
or another, but he moved the last box from my tip-toes.

'Sink it.'

Perhaps a daemon lead him from unsolicited greetings?
Then he dipped his rod and drowned the line. The speaker
flicked me a glance, a look that rejected familiarity, someone
whose intimacies ended badly and had reduced them to a tic.
Detectable to those in pain's orbit, but absent to the rest.

I lingered but it didn't matter; space, disputed and
mortgaged, was not his field; his boundary was a crimson
rod, scattered boxes and a carapace body.

The antennae had four inches of black and white bands, a
chub hit on the drop or the lift when his V2 rocket wavered
– I saw nothing. No aesthete but efficient enough: a skip cap,
Hush Puppies, a go-faster coat. You get anglers like that, a
Galapagos of technique but they're rare. He said something.

It was him.

The other me, the one if I'd stayed, hunched and shouting
nothings at no-one, the wintered man. The one who chose
not to make mistakes or feel remorse, not to feel but to fish
his rum pitch until he couldn't fish the spiteful river any more.

The café was still there with its bantam Niagara but the weir
roared now; she'd been tripped, pushed by the spate, you
could see her soiled undergarments beneath the dirty apron
weed-strewn, yellowed. Foul smelling. An empty manor stood
at the end of the tree-line waiting for a sturgeon who marked
a death in the household. The bone-headed fish lost, the family
gone and their successors scared off by revenants – I'd taken
a good pike here. Hard against the wall, sink-and-draw in
the grand style while the torrent threw up pocket rainbows.

Then I followed the canal where the dirigible carp rose. An escapee from the gravel pit sucking a cheese sandwich before sinking back to the flood leaving my heart slamming ribs for a way out.

Some mischief is intentional, sown traps carefully tended till they take root and bud; that was what I thought this was about, a long toothache from a sweet offering I should have left years before. A slight I watered and added my compost to but the river has up-ended me. The lopsided path has its own tale and regret boils to a simmer with each step.

The opposite bank looks like any other, a flat field with six feet of sandstone tumble. A record came out of its cow-backed pasture, bream by the stone. A river's summer pact; a bounty before uncaring Friesians – now willows hang gifts and tokens: half a doll like Paris Hilton, Lidl bags, tinsel, last year's mono with BB pendants, winter spoils.

The chippie kid who'd cast himself adrift was here. A thread was caught and he'd almost unravelled himself before I looked back and followed it to the centre of his earth. The torn pages needed mending. Peter never became Mr. C. He'd slunk off when he got snagged, the paternoster broken with the other lost boys.

Two rods came out the car and I walked to the sunk thorn and the eddies. One bait went in the margins and the other as far as the lead would hold. If the winter river beat me he'd be master, crowing.

I'd missed a run. The yellow drop-off had fallen but the alarm couldn't work itself past a low growl, a hound upset by a tomcat in the yard. Probably an eel dragging the bait backwards all the way to the Sargasso. The boils were a cauldron; snow flurries threatened to take the rods out of their rest.

Now.

And now.

She was still taking line when I stuck and headed straight

for the thorn. I chinned her out. About 6lb, nicked in the scissors.

It was time to move on. The starlings knew it. Time to leave the chalk face, the guru racket and the cold trail that lead me here. Goodbye Mr Chippie.

Pan is Dead

A secret cleft. As secret as a newsreader's shoes, as impenetrable as Mina Harker, the lake was none of these. Where two-million-year-old gravel deposits were gouged in a decade, holiday cabins sprang. If John Wayne had gone looking for Cheryl from Girls Aloud instead of Natalie Wood in *The Searchers*, he might have left such a dwelling. A pre-dawn full English to a piped rap track in the clubhouse, stomach boiling like an acid murderer's bath, slot machines twittering blanks, a plasma-screen weatherman with the head of the Rhodes Colossus promises rain from karaoke speakers. A trip to the gents for a minute's peace but flushers flush, lights illuminate, vents suck loud enough for ear protection as a poltergeist of automation watches me pee. This is 24-hour fun-land. Lord Snooty has just been dropped in a manga comic.

I don't care how big the fish are, I don't do Klondikes, neither Le Mans boat starts, nor stupid o'clock, but somehow I was in for a weekend's *Blade Runner* fishing. Someone, maybe, heard a 30 had come out. Yeah, well. There was one hole it might fit and I wasn't sitting on it, I was lobbing soft baits into a corner of a gaping mineral deposit wound hoping last night's Triple-X would stay down.

At least it was quiet here and still too early for bedside tables to creak up their morning-after pills, too early for money rows, for snooker, for generators to fill pneumatic grottos and, where I was, hopefully too far away when they did. Pylons stalked the horizon against a magenta sky I hadn't seen since the 1970 World Cup on my auntie's rental Pye.

Every house in the eastern counties says the wind from the Urals stops by, but my morning was last night in Murmansk. England wasn't dreaming, it was on a mortician's slab.

The Next Big Water is usually a godforsaken compensating reservoir or the skelly-riddled thermo-cline of some sour loch where eight GDR pike stuff themselves to an early grave. Under the tilt of sponsored baseball caps, the cheery bonhomie of men who'd cross-cast your Ernie as soon as look at you chase grotesques, men with reputations and a retainer and live-bait so free-roaming they've forgotten they were ever hooked. Then I long for ponds with pike like a pencil, not third trimester super-moms in April fecund. Pike with stripes before stock rainbows distend them and send form into hiding so function reigns unchallenged.

    That of course, is why I'll always be a bit shit as an angler. Betjeman, Eric Coates, Edith Sitwell reading *Façade* from the glow of a car radio with the heater on scorch, I craved warm nuns and inglenooks, things I've left behind or never had but I was fishing in bleach with a theramin track from the wires of the national grid and getting RSI from twitching Burts. Then I had a follow. When you've cast rubber baits at the same spot for an hour a pike from the Pleistocene layer is a bit of a shock. One second you're a penny-a-go brass monkey automaton, the next you're a daft kid believing like Peter Pan. When you strip away the crap, the TV, the kitchen sink, the retail parks – what are you left with? William Blake, Powell and Pressburger, Kate Bush, The Fall, Robert Wyatt, the love of a good woman, the smile of your kids and stupidly big fish. The man with a child in his eyes wanted them as much as all those others. When a voice shouted 'Pan is Dead' from the Greek coast a few millennia back he'd probably been fishing Bulldawgs here. I should have listened to the Colossus from the weather centre. It was the last pike I saw all weekend.

Andrew Greig

I was introduced to fly fishing by my friend Mal Duff, for whom it was his greatest passion after mountaineering. When he died on Everest, my apprenticeship was incomplete and still is. The great Scottish poet Norman MacCaig, a very accomplished fisherman, shortly before his death in 1996 asked me to fish on his behalf in his favourite place on Earth, the Loch of the Green Corrie in Assynt, Sutherland. 'If you succeed, I shall be delighted. If you fail, then looking down from a place in which I do not believe, I shall be most amused.' This quest led to several trips with friends to Assynt, which in turn has grown into a full-scale book incorporating fishing expeditions, elements of biography, memoir, history and geology, plus musings on friendship, poetry, mortality, love and malt whisky. *At the Loch of the Green Corrie,* from which the following pieces are excerpted and slightly adapted, will be published by Quercus in 2010.

Andrew Greig is the author of six collections of poetry, the latest of which is *This Life, This Life: New and Selected Poems*, published by Bloodaxe Books. His six novels are *That Summer, Electric Brae, The Return of John McNab, When They Lay Bare, In Another Light and Romanno Bridge*. His latest work of non-fiction is *Preferred Lies*. He lives in Edinburgh and Orkney.

First Cast at the
Loch of the Green Corrie

We drop our packs on a little promontory at the north end of the Loch of the Green Corrie and stand there, absorbing our surroundings.

My first reaction: it's not pretty. Nor particularly green. When MacCaig said it was his favourite place in all Assynt and asked me to fish here on his behalf, I'd imagined some blue jewel cupped in a green setting, a radiant brooch pinned high on the bosom of a great hill, looking out over a monumental gathering of other stellar mountains. But despite the coarse grass that grows among the boulders and bedrock, the overall effect is grey and austere.

We are very enclosed here. On three sides, slopes fall steeply to a rough fringe around the loch. Down the slopes across from us drape shrouds of grey scree, probably quartzite eroded from the summit. Now the sun has gone in, that scree lends the clear water its colour. There are no flowers, no blooming heather, no trees, bushes or bird life. At 1,800 feet, the breeze is strikingly cool. If this is the Green Corrie I'd hate to see the Grey one.

Shrugging on his fleece, Andy hunkers down at the water's edge, dabbles his fingers in, licks.

'Perfect alkalinity,' he pronounces. 'There are definitely fish in here.'

We get cracking.

It's a bit like when you meet someone's new love, I think while tying on a new Black Pennel fly. You look and listen, and wonder what the fuss is about. He or she seems a perfectly ordinary person. This seems another Highland loch, a bit more remote and bleak than most. It must have hidden charms. Or maybe it just has loads of easy-to-catch fish.

I go through my small fly box and pick out a Blue Zulu as the bob-fly, the one nearest to me. I select a nameless dowdy bit of fluff as the mid-fly, aware that Peter and Andy already have their lines out. We all want to be the first person to catch Norman's fish.

'If you catch a fish, I shall be delighted. If you fail, then, looking down from a place in which I do not believe, I shall be most amused.'

I hurriedly attach the cast to the line. In this cool breeze there is no sign of any bug life above or on the water. Maybe that's what MacAskill meant by it being no use if the wind's from the East, the chilly direction. And these flies look like nothing that ever flew or swam. I have to trust that trout, like ourselves, rise to metaphor. Or are instinctively curious.

I stand on a mossy rock beside the promontory and trail the flies in the water to get them wet and heavy. I can see all the stones on the bottom, never clearer. Andy is already working the shore to my right, Peter on the other side. Their lines roll out straight and silent, drop lightly onto the bright choppy surface.

My fishing apprenticeship with Mal Duff had been entirely from boats, where casting is less critical. But maybe I'll get lucky. At the very least I'll learn and get better. Hoping Peter and Andy aren't watching, hoping that the invisible dead aren't watching, though in my mind they always are, I murmur *For you* and set the line flying.

We were so eager, fresh to the place, wondering who was going to be first to catch that fish for Norman. A single fish, caught by any one of us, would fulfil the mission, but it would be good to be the one who caught it.

The first ten, the first twenty minutes passed. The sun came full out. We shrugged off our fleeces, tied them round waists and continued. Andy sighed and moved further along the bank; Peter stepped out onto a rock and cast further towards the still centre of the loch. Caught in a swirl of inattention, my cast tangled.

I knelt on the coarse grass, squinted at the pale fine line. Took off my glasses and looked closer – my father's gesture, one I was starting to make more often, like that soft involuntary sound as I stood up or sat down.

I got lucky. It was only a fankle, not a bourach – the dowdy mid-fly and the radiant Blue Zulu had involuntary mated in a tangle of metaphors. I cut off the mid-fly. Keep it simple.

A cry from Andy.

'Rise!'

I looked up in time to see the ripple spread.

'Big one,' Peter commented. I got my line out with fresh urgency. It helped to know there was something down there.

Another rise, this time not out in the middle where Peter was casting, but in close.

'Tiddler,' he commented.

Then another. I caught the flicker, then the small plop came in on the breeze. It was close in again, in the shallows on Andy's side. He cursed quietly but we were all cheered by the action, and religiously shifted our casts to the shallow margins.

For a while, nothing much happened.

Busy casting, it took some time to realise the loch had gone dead. For an hour or more there had been no further rises. Not a bite, not a nibble for any of us.

Peter picked his way along the shore towards me.

'It happens sometimes,' he said. *'If you don't enjoy fishing when you don't catch a fish, you shouldn't be a fisherman.'*

Andy shrugged and took his line in. We sprawled on the little promontory, ate flapjacks and drank tea, and looked at the loch. The sun came out again, the cool wind dropped. For a while we just lay and looked and no one said anything. We were, I believe, entirely happy.

The Loch of the Green Corrie has a silence that is not silent. Lying there I can hear air drift through heather and over rock and water. Air and invisible streams are gathered and reflected back by the slopes that soar around us, as though we lie within a giant ear. It's what used to happen when the needle came down on the record's empty grooves: the sound of presence.

Its surroundings are without trees or shrubs, but there are tiny flowers hidden among the heather. Devoid of animal life, but we have seen many tiny frogs on the way here. No songbirds, but twice a hoodie crow has drifted over, offered a harsh kaak and was gone.

It is very still; the loch and the hills aren't going anywhere. Yet the water still shifts up and down on the pebbles below, the coarse grass stirs, clouds re-form even as we assign shapes to them. Peter turns another page of *Autumn of the Patriarch*; Andy flicks at a bluebottle, props himself up on his elbow and stares at the loch as if he could will fish to rise.

This place is as stripped of decoration as a Free Presbyterian church.

Yet MacCaig and AK MacLeod, both devout atheists, had loved it beyond all other places. When Norman's body could no longer make it up here, he attended faithfully in his mind. The light in his eyes, when on that last occasion I asked him what his favourite spot on Earth was, and he finally answered '*I think it has to be the loch of the Green Corrie,*' shines on the water here.

I should have guessed the loch's virtues would be subtle ones. MacCaig liked austerity, the classical over the flowery and romantic. The plainness of this place of water, stone and turf offers not so much sensory deprivation as amplification. Eyes, ears, body itself, have to tune to nuance, to the tiny splash of pink flower, the single distant croak. Perhaps that heightening is what MacCaig so valued here. It certainly wasn't easy-to-catch fish.

Andy stirs. 'Right, I'm going to the side Peter was on, where that big one rose.'

Peter grunts, marks his place with a blade of grass and puts Marquez aside for later.

Clearly we are going to be some time here.

Just for a change, I snip off the Blue Zulu – never believed in that fly anyway, why would a fish? – and tie on something grey and greenish as being in tune with our surroundings. I get up stiffly, flex my right shoulder to work off that stab under the shoulder blade, and go back to work again.

Fair enough, I think. If this was easy, it would mean less.

An involuntary cry from Peter. His rod is curved. Then another cry, the rod straightens. His shoulders drop.

'Curses,' he says.

'Big one?' Andy calls.

Peter shrugs.

'So-so.'

'What did it take?'

'The Pennel.'

Andy quickly takes in his line and kneels over his fly box.

We fish hard, in silence, keeping an eye on each other. One of Norman MacAskill's few offerings before I left Lochinver was how inventive MacCaig was with the barbs and insults when someone failed to land their fish through slowness or inattention.

'Sometimes in Latin or Greek, which was not fair. Mind you, he lost a few fish himself. Then myself or AK would tell him off in the Gaelic.'

'Did you talk a lot on these trips?' I asked in the hope of more stories.

'No, mostly we fished.'

I'm haunted by the knowledge that the three of them, MacCaig, MacAskill and AK, came here, as we three are here now, some thirty years later. They came, as we do, to be out in the hills, to fish, to be in each other's company, mostly wordlessly. They would have been the age we are now. I can almost see their shades quicken in the stir of air over the grass, hear them in the chuckle of water by my foot. Time passes in cast and retrieve. Light on water, cloud reflection and sunlight broken on the water. The sense of where we are, where this is, is sinking in. We are absorbing it, though it feels as though the place is absorbing us.

The afternoon wears on. Mist crawls down over the shoulder of the hill and slithers over the grass to us. A breeze comes with it, and within minutes fingers go white. There have been no more rises. Peter's nibble is as close as we've got.

With hats and fleeces, we take another tea-break, huddle out of the breeze and discuss it. We have covered the entire loch. Nothing is happening out there. We have attended and done our best. If necessary, we come back tomorrow.

'One more hour?' Andy says. 'Let's really go to it.'

We get stiffly to our feet, flex knees and fingers then pick up our rods and take our stances around the loch. Standing on little promontories of pleasure and fatigue, poised somewhere between faith and hope and doubt, we send our wavering lines out over the water.

A Bourach on Loch na Gainmhich

Along the shore from me, silhouetted into glowing coal against the fierce sunset light spanking the loch, Andy curses quietly. He flicks his rod once more then stops, his line thick with tangle, the three flies caught in a cage of doodles. I am relieved this happens to much better fishermen than me. I do well to cast for twenty minutes before the line snags. The right thing to do is stop immediately; the natural reaction is to flick the rod again in the hope the line will unsnag. This never happens.

As Andy sighs, lays down his rod and sits to address the problem, I give the lamb stew a last stir then go and stand beside him.

'Guddle or a fankle?'

'Bourach,' he says firmly, and takes out his knife. Further round the loch, Peter retrieves, sends his near-invisible line out to drop three flies seductively on the broken water. He can see what has happened; it will give him a clear ten or fifteen minutes fishing while his brother sorts this out. He is not actually gloating, just amused.

'A total bourach,' Andy mutters, still struggling to untangle his nylon cast from the thicker floating line. He tells me his father, a keen etymologist and author of several books on Scottish place and family names, gave him the word. A 'fankle' is a tangle that has a chance, with patience and persistence, of being sorted. A 'bourach', pronounced with those tones of doomed resignation that come so naturally to the Scottish voice, is irreversible. Nothing to be done but cut off the flies, remove the ruined cast and set up a new one.

As Peter leisurely quarters the water, working the area, Andy snicks the flies off the doomed line, lays them on his knee. Two Blue Zulus, one Black Pennel. They do not look like any insect I have ever seen. Perhaps trout vision is poor? But it's clear they are extremely fussy: wrong fly, no fish.

Maybe the flies stand as metaphor or far-fetched yet appealing simile for the thing they are not: a hint, a vivid reminder, something to stir the jaded palette of trout or men. Poetry in general, and Norman MacCaig's in particular, does this a lot: a bird fires notes from its soft pea-shooter, a toad looks like a purse, a wild rose bush is a tattered pirate with a bright parrot on its shoulder.

Which of course it is not. Simile and metaphor are creative lies, lures to catch the mind's fish by. MacCaig's sensibility was agile with them, and his intellect was often infuriated by this very talent. He constantly reminds us and himself the natural world is what it is, not like something else nor a metaphor for anything. Its very *is*-ness is its essence and its value. Even to name the frog, the dog, the rose bush, is to lose it.

And yet, and yet it is what we do. And this figurative language, these images, similes, metaphors on which so much poetry rests, makes the world new to us again. The rose bush is not a pirate, but my God we look at it again and smile inwardly. Norman repeated this trick, this re-freshing of vision and feeling, all over this Assynt landscape, laying out his bright, improbable lures. Being here is like living inside his skull.

A low cry comes downwind from Peter. His rod flicks back once, twice, then his shoulders drop. 'Bigger one,' he calls. 'Lost it.' He casts again, the grey line curls out behind him, flows forward, dips with a silent sigh.

Andy works faster. As he ties on the tail fly to the new cast, I wonder: when our lives get tangled, how are we to know what we can sort out and what we should abandon?

'Right,' Andy says. 'There are big fish down the far end, and I'm going to catch them.'

He sets off along the shore, ever-optimistic, confident he knows fankle from bourach.

John Andrews

John Andrews writes about angling history for a variety of periodicals from *Waterlog* to *The Field*, as well as running www.andrewsofarcadia – a website selling vintage fishing tackle for the soul. The following pieces are extracts from *Tunnyland*, a book he has been working on for the last five years.

Tunnyland

1

Sixty miles north by north east of the dirty jewel of Scarborough, far out in the North Sea, beyond the Silver Pit, the bright electric glow of the yacht Nahlin lights up the night sky. It is August 1933, the middle of a heatwave, a summer of lightning strikes, white speedboats, sea monsters and of a message in a bottle:

'Been in a rowing boat without oars since 11th'

In the corner of the Nahlin's ballroom stands Gladys Meryl Yule, the world's richest heiress. Under her bias-cut chiffon dress her skin is a brilliant white, a film of fine powder, sprinkled with flecks of glitter. She sparkles like an exotic animal, an escaped trapeze artist from the circus of Schiaparelli. A genie from a bottle. The kind you might rub if you could wish for anything in the world. The palms of Meryl's hands are spread out in front of her and are moving in time to the rhythm. Beneath her angular black hair her eyes are closed as she listens to the frenzied playing of the band. As with all parties this season, this one started on the stroke of midnight. Raucous laughter, shouts and screams come at her from every side. There are women dressed like her and men dressed like her. The sunseekers. Meryl feels the familiar chemical kick in her stomach and the dizzy rush in her head. A slight nausea she has come to enjoy. The lights behind her eyes changing colour. As she opens them once again she finds it hard to focus. The light from the chandeliers is so brilliant, so intense, it threatens to burn everything out. Then she is seized by the arm and the waist and carried into the middle of the dance floor. The feeling of an unwanted hand pressing hard into the small of her back. Her fingers gripped with an intent. A whirlwind before she finds a place to rest. An arm of an zebra-skin chair, the edge of a glass-topped table. More drink, more drink, a cigarette, the comforting hiss of the tobacco being lit and the cool smoke slowing everything down. People entering and leaving the room, adjusting their hair and brushing down their clothes. Some now half-dressed and dancing with a new abandon. Speed, speed, speed. The band is a four-piece playing the latest tune, the rumba, over and over again, the tempo rising with each turn. There is a monkey on the drums and one on the piano, red fezs balanced on their heads, shrieking with approval, their teeth glistening in the light. Meryl watches it all, the bubbles from her champagne rising to the top of the glass in a perfect and endless stream.

From outside, beyond the bright light, from the darkness of the deck below there is a scream. An unnatural and inhuman cry, of horror and alarm. Nobody above hears it for the music and the noise of the party. It is the monkeys who are first to sense there is something wrong. The monkey behind the drums stands up on its hind legs and runs across the room and under a table. There it covers its eyes with its hands. Its companion follows until they are crouched together in a tiny huddle, shaking. Then comes the scream again, this time from inside the ballroom. The sound of glass smashing as drinks are dropped. The frantic closing of windows. But it is too late, the room is now alive with winged insects, giant buzzing stick-boned intruders, hovering towards the glow of the chandeliers. Their wings making a rasping sound as they vibrate. Perching on people's heads and crawling over their bare arms and legs. Soon they have a choreography of their own, a dance of their own as they fill the room by their hundreds.

Meryl Yule rushes out onto the deck. There in the moonlight she can see the intensity of the swarm, so thick it threatens to blacken the moon in the sky. It is only then that Meryl realizes how warm the night is. The air is from another place, the deserts of Northern Africa, blown here by some far-off Scirroco. Dry, warm and scented. The swarm is settling on the wood and on the metal, this island of heat in the middle of a cold sea, until there is not an inch of deck which is not covered by a resting insect. Meryl lies adorned by them, not twitching, not daring to move a muscle, her heart beating out of her chest as she breathes. A statue from a midsummer night's dream in a locust storm.

An hour later Meryl's reverie is broken by an imploring voice from the sea below. 'It's time tiv go, miss.' Meryl opens her eyes, looks down and sees the outline of a human figure in a rowing boat. Dressed in rough baggy trousers, a sweater tight over a barrel chest, and a cap upon his head. There is a familiarity present that belongs only to this place. Without a second thought Meryl shakes the last of the insects from her skin and climbs down the ladder into the arms of the figure in the boat. 'Good night, was it? You'll be cold dressed like that, miss.' The figure puts a coat around her shoulders and steadies her hand as Meryl finds her seat. Then she turns and looks at her companion. He smiles and the brown smudge of his skin cracks with a smile. He lights her a rolled cigarette which Meryl takes with the tips of her fingers onto her lips, shivering inside with delight. She settles into her borrowed coat as she is rowed away from her home, its occupants now silent after their racket-filled night. Every now and again an insect rising up from the deck and flying into the air, searching for the first rays of sun of the new day.

The drifters surround the yacht, twin masted wooden tubs with a single funnel and crews of ten, Dutch boys and Yarmouth men. They work only at night, the trawlers by day. In an hour the drifters' work will be done. Meryl's oarsman hollers up to the men on the deck of the first drifter they come to. 'Hulloa, any tunny?'

'Naa,' comes the answer. Then a drifterman points to another vessel a hundred yards away. It is flashing a light on and off. The oarsman turns the small rowing boat out from the shadow of the drifter. Before they reach the flashing light they see a brilliant silver explosion beneath their feet. It is the flank of a giant sea monster, the tunny, the bluefin tuna, a visitor from a faraway place, brought from the coast of Portugal up into the North Sea by the Gulf Stream drift.

Eyes stolen from a medieval fresco, chain mail flank from the armour of a crusader, tail of a dragon. Feeding lustfully on the herring shoal. Friend and curse of the driftermen. Quarry of the sunseekers.

Meryl Yule struggles with the leather harness. Its leather is rough against her skin but soon she is strapped into her wooden seat. The fishing rod in her hand is heavy, although it is attached to a socket in her seat. Her elegant muscles arch all the way along her bare arms. Meryl lowers the bait, a whole mackerel, into the water, in the way that Edward Peel taught her. The bait sits in the oily swell. There are thousands of spent herring scales in the water, sparkling like the glitter upon her skin. She is mermaid and hunter. Angel and goddess. There is a slight buzz in the back of her head, like a live electric charge spitting, waiting for a connection. Suddenly there is a flash like sunlight off a mirror and the rod she is holding is nearly torn out of her hands. 'It's on, miss.' Meryl can feel her oarsman fighting to keep their tiny rowing boat in check but it is being pulled by the seahorse she has just hooked. At the same time it is tearing fifty, one hundred, two hundred, three hundred yards of line from her reel and still towing the boat. Away from the fleet of driftermen and their cheers and whistles. Just her and Tom Pashby and their runaway train. From the security of the Nahlin and out into the horizonless blue ocean, to a place far off any known map. To a place called Tunnyland.

2

Eight miles east of the Yorkshire coastal town of Scarborough the Gulf Stream Drift flows against the prevailing current of the North Sea. Past the Silver Pit and out towards the Dogger Bank with its seemingly endless shoals of herring, a city on the sea, the commercial fishing capital of dynasties of fishing families from Holland and Yarmouth. Men who fill the holds of their boats until the weight threatens to bring the sea over the keel. This is a kingdom of salt water and superstition, mountainous seas and blue wheelhouses, boats and lucky knives. Of an industrious people who live on a flotilla of steam drifters divided up between the fishing grounds.

It is an early morning in 1929. High above the two bays of Scarborough town a man of fifty-seven stands in the salt-bleached long grass of the Yorkshire moorland looking out to sea. In his ears is the sound of the wind. It is a particular sound which the man feels belongs to this stretch of coastline. He is dressed simply in an old woollen suit and worn-in leather shoes. He wears a pastor's style black felt hat upon his head and around him is slung a canvas and leather game bag. He has no companions. He is William J Clarke, a resident of Scarborough, a naturalist by profession and a fiercely passionate collector and recorder of the oddities of nature. In the parlour of his small home at 51 Oak Road he poses at night with his pet boa constrictor around his shoulders. It has neither hands or feet to play with his ears and his hair. He has neither wife nor lover at whom to smile.

Born in the town of Scarborough in 1871, William J Clarke is the son of a bottle maker and livestock dealer. He has inherited a scientific love of nature from his parents. Aged ten, he joins a naturalists' club at primary school. A year later, at the Frederick York Richmond school in Scarborough, Clarke becomes the keeper of the aquarium. To raise funds for its upkeep he organizes soirées in the Grand Hotel. It is here aged twelve that he gives his first public speech, on the subject of reptiles. He leaves school at fourteen and works in the offices of the *Scarborough Gazette* working double shifts and earns enough money to buy the lease on a shop at 44 Huntriss Row eight years later in 1893. Here he becomes Scarborough's first taxidermist. He fills his shop window with stuffed birds, seagulls in flight, puffins with orange beaks and cased fish from the rivers and meres of the county. Behind the glass of the front door to the shop are framed photographs of freakish Victoriana from around the world, two-headed snakes and mock-ups of mermaids. Much of the stock comes via the channels of the Scarborough Natural History Society which Clarke set up on the night of the 4th November 1889 in a room above a stationer's shop with five other men: Gyngell, Hargreaves, Parker, Rines and Rowntree. Together they wrote a press release which they sent out to all of the local newspapers and journals. In it was a request for information on any unusual natural discoveries near Scarborough. The men were overwhelmed with replies. Soon they had created an unofficial network of scavengers, from poachers to shepherds, from coastguards to costermongers, men who knock on the door at 51 Oak Road late at night with reports of monsters on the beach and beasts upon the moor. Men who are greeted by William Clarke wearing a smoking jacket, his scaled companion curled around his neck.

Mostly, such reports are fantasies, driven by the temptation of a reward. Indeed, many of the early years of the Society are largely uneventful. In the Society's published journal, *The Naturalist*, Clarke writes essays on birds' eggs and albino hedgehogs. He compiles notes on the nesting sites of peregrine falcons and multiple broods of blackbirds. But as the twenty-fifth anniversary of the society dawns in 1914, things begin to change. On the night of 29th June a salmon netsman called Richardson is collecting the catch from his nets in Filey Bay. As he does so he notices something odd trapped in the netting. It is a sea creature of several feet in length, shaped he would later say 'like a bass fiddle'. Instinctively, Richardson tries to free the creature, but as soon as he touches it he is knocked to the sand by an enormous electrical shock. He tries once more but again he is shocked. Cutting the net around the capture Richardson leaves it on the sand to die. On his return to the town later that evening he mentions the incident to some men standing outside a pub. Some of Clarke's networkers are among the group and proceed to the beach. Gripping the dead fish by the tips of its wings they parade it through the streets of Filey, knocking on every door to show people this new invader.

On the same night, in his home at 51 Oak Road in the neighbouring town of Scarborough, William Clarke pours a drink for the skipper of a local herring drifter. The man sits in front of an empty grate, nervously eyeing the snake curled up in the armchair next to him. The man has come to Clarke for a charm. Clarke's collection of such things is legendary. In card boxes in his home he has dozens and dozens of relics: eel skins, pigeons' hearts, a velvet bag containing the tooth of a dead man and dragon's blood from the Congo. Recently he has begun to collect fragments of high-explosive German shell as a charm against the war. Clarke is used to giving fishermen decorated lead weights to bring them good catches. But it is none of these that the fisherman wants. He will only trade his knowledge for Neptune's Tooth, that of a sea urchin, known by fishermen everywhere as a charm against drowning. How badly he needs it. A white-handled knife is no longer enough. Not one of his eight crew can swim. They know to keep the hatches shut or else they will be thrown into the sea. Apart from that they are carefree and move about more easily on the deck than on dry land. But since the events of the previous few weeks they have become nervous and withdrawn. They are reluctant to bring in the nets. There is something attacking the catch as it is hauled. It only seems to happen at night but even then in the light from their own boats and others the men are terrified. The speed at which the nets are grabbed is immense. At first the men think it might be a huge shark but the nets are never badly damaged. There are no teeth marks. On occasions when it is calm the sea around the drifters boils, as if the ships are being circled deliberately. There are rumours that it may be some remote mechanical device, a sea rocket, that the Germans have invented and are testing in the North Sea.

Clarke lets the man finish his drink and pours him another. He then leaves the room and climbs the stairs. Past the Georgian prints of oarfish, long sea serpents who would enravel the masts of sailing ships and take them down, drowning all of the crew. Past the collection of monkeys' skulls fixed to the wall in the space above Clarke's bedroom door. Clarke has a particular fascination with monkeys, and these skulls are from his favourite strain, the squirrel. He traded a broken brass pocket watch for them with a man in the Newcastle Steam Packet Public House who had recently returned from the far east. Clarke notices how different they look each time he passes underneath them, their smiling teeth lit eerily by the gaslamp that hisses quietly over the stairs.

The drifter skipper leaves 51 Oak Road and for the first time in his life walks away from the direction of the harbour and up Lightfoots towards Seamer Moor. Despite the charm which he has wrapped in one of William Clarke's silk handkerchiefs and tucked into the pocket of his jacket, he is nervous and reluctant to return immediately to his boat and to the sea. He feels a sudden longing for the safety and comfort of the land. To be as high up as possible. To look out over everything. He walks and walks, staggering into a darkness unfamiliar to him. Noticing how the stars in the sky are not as bright inland as they are out at sea. He continues on until the lights of the town have grown faint behind him.

Beyond them across the South Sands, beneath Scarborough Castle, the sea rolls in ceaselessly. Mile after mile of it. Chasing the skipper with a low hiss. Far out in the greyness is harboured the monster of which the skipper lives in fear. Within a space of only a few months this creature will make the town of Scarborough as exotic and glamorous a destination for the international glitterati as the Riviera. A place which William Clarke will help to make famous and of which Meryl Yule will be crowned princess. As William Clarke was later to write in his journal, 'It was the summer of 1914 that I first began to receive from the local fishermen reports of strange fish. The like of which they had never seen before. I had almost forgotten the incidents until the summer of 1929.'

William Wyatt

I grew up in East London between two rivers, the Lea and the Roding. This was where I cut my angling teeth, chasing impossible-to-catch wily old chub or else luring crucians from Epping Forest bomb holes. I've been fishing as long as I can remember, discovering early the ability to escape life's tribulations by having a burning desire to catch fish, and all which that entails. Only recently I discovered that when not on the bank I could actually write about my angling forays and experiences. I moved abroad in the late nineties to escape the hedonistic fall-out of the early nineties. I'm a fair-weather angler by nature, with a love for simple, sporting and above all else poetic angling.

Pond Life 1

The lure of the pond on the green, its strange magnetic pull that made a young boy get up before light, leave the old camping bed, woodchip and heartbreak, and run the gauntlet of nonces and stop-outs. The odd glimpse by the island margin was enough. It could hold me for months. I'd once tried wading over to get a better angle, only to find myself waist-deep in muddy crap. The pigmy tench and feral goldfish kept me amused, satisfied in between sightings. She'd broken me on numerous occasions, totally out of the blue, every time like the last. In hindsight she must have only gone seven or eight pounds, but my lack of experience and unsatisfactory tackle always resulted in yet another scar on my conscience and a lost peacock quill float.

One morning I sat there watching for lift-bites as the sun rose and the traffic gathered momentum. An old escort van pulled over and a pair of old boys with plastic buckets and stout tackle appeared. The skinny one of the two started to peg out a keepnet, the other made his way round to me in a shifty shuffle, head like an ox with a rolly hanging out a corner of mouth.

'A'right son, done any good?'

He looked once at me and then started scrutinising my net.

'Naa! Just a few bites, mate.'

'I tell you what son, I'll give you a nicker a fish, me an me Brother Brian over there. We're up from Canvey, looking to stock his missus' pond, if you know what I mean.'

A few quid wouldn't have gone amiss, but it felt a little like selling your gran's dog. It felt wrong. After matey's proposition, bites dwindled off in a fierce July sun. I packed up, went home. I never saw that carp again. I like to think she either remained out of sight or maybe died. But she probably spent her last days flopping about in some tacky koi pond on Canvey Island. Whatever the truth, her disappearance left me infected, haunted and a little sad.

❖ ❖ ❖

It was fucking quiet down the Napier. Just a couple of young lads playing pool, the odd piss-head at the bar. We sat in the usual spot, tucked away behind the door, a cosy nook that let us survey the place unseen, shooting the breeze and getting slowly inebriated. Paul Weller's *Stanley Road* on the jukebox, a pint in my hand, sitting in my usual spot, back to the wall, I take stock of my fishing gang.

To my right is Floyd. An odd fellow whose demise and present state of mind is, I believe, due to an unfortunate love affair. Some blame the acid for his raging schizophrenia. Instead, it is the direct product of his girlfriend getting knobbed by a mate – not present at our table I might add, in case you suspect your narrator. Julia was only fourteen at the time, daughter of a wealthy car dealer and a mother who appreciated large quantities of freebase coke, riding horses and nice black fellows. Juls broke old Floyd's heart and wiped the remains on the curve. So there you have it: Floyd, schizo hobbit, alcoholic, brain fried by the purple tin and copious amounts of crap ecstasy and not having a bunk-up since Juls. Poor fellow, heart of gold, favourite food red onion in pitta bread with lashings of ketchup. Could be down to the fact he never has a pot to piss in, and kebab meat would set him back an extra fifty pence, half a pint in F's world.

Floyd's angling experience: none whatsoever.

To my left sits Danny, a mechanic by day, full-blown heroin addict the rest of the time, always on hand, cock like a fucking baguette. A very friendly and altogether obliging grease monkey. As well as a healthy smack habit he's got this taste for fast motors. And he's an over-sexual Tom Petty fan. Dan's latest craze is his Renault 5 GT turbo, and fucking prostitutes up their arseholes. It's enough to put you off your pint if you're not that way inclined. The bastard waxes lyrical about it. Costs him more than smack and the car loan put together. Oh and of course his hallowed Tuesday nights at the Camden Palace, a regular haunt for our band of merry men. The place to go midweek and pick up soapy tourists for whatever sordid whim you have in mind. I've probably said enough all ready.

Danny's angling experience: caught a trout from a Scottish lock aged eight, never been fishing since.

Now Jon, sitting to Danny's left. Well, matters of the flesh don't interest him so hysterically. Jon, unsuccessful petty criminal, plastic drug addict, loves the kudos but can't afford a habit. An altogether untrustworthy character, starts fights but don't have the minerals to finish them. He started this fight at some gig a while back. Once he clocked he was out-numbered, the fucker only pretended to have an epileptic fit, a devious and clever escape artist, with Oscar-winning abilities. A rare case, a bully secure in himself, but we keep him on a tight leash. Alarmingly he has a very attractive sister whom he protects religiously, but doesn't seem to mind her giving head to unsavoury yardie gangsters in exchange for a gram of white. But if you buy her as much as a shandy, he starts throwing teddies.

Jon's angling experience: none.

Moving on, to Jon's left, is Jeff. All-round dodger, he's just got up to take a piss as usual. Mr Squeaky Clean. Free from the shackles of most available vice, his serotonin levels intact, healthy libido and master of the missionary position. He's got a fucking huge record collection and a healthy bank account, due largely to the fact he still lives at home with his mum, getting his socks ironed in addition to three well-balanced, nutritious meals a day. A ladies' man, don't ask me why. I can't see how having what look like fish fingers on the side of yer head could possibly do for the fairer sex, but the bastard always brings home something he has to sneak past mother in the morning.

Angling experience: a few times out with me stalking carp, and some limited time behind a spinning rod whilst at his nan's place down on the east coast.

Next to Jeff's pint-dodging empty seat we have the Rabbi, Jew boy, naa! Not your stereotypical ten to two, fork in the sugar bowl, selection kipots, Friday evenings spent down the synagogue – oh no, not this Jew. He loves spending money, eating bacon butties and purchasing vintage cars. In his procession just now a lovely Mini Cooper and MGB Roadster. He earns a fortune, inherited a fortune, The Rabbi is the man to see if you need to borrow a few quid. Mr Corporate Solutions, with a half-secret: a passion for rap music and graffiti. He's known to steal car paint from Homebase or B&Q, listening to KRS-One on the Walkman, then to go spray things on tube trains in the middle of the night. By breakfast time he's suited and booted waiting on the platform towing the line, in a wall of commuters, as his night's handy work, sorry R, artwork, rolls in, whisking him off into the big shitty for a day's pen-pushing.

The Rabbi's angling experience: a handful of childhood brushes with perch. Been out with me wandering the banks of the Roding scaring chub, and a spot of unfruitful carp fishing.

Johnny helps himself to a third of Jeff's ciggies, just returning the pack and lighter to its original place on the beer mat seconds before J returns. Danny raises an eyebrow, making him look ridiculously like some kind of dreadlocked hippy Bond villain as he peers over the top of his *Auto Trader*.

'What's everyone having then?' Jeff says as he clocks a fresh round.

'Took a shit, you tight-arse?' Danny splutters.

J just shruggs it off as usual, like piss on a duck's back, smiles and makes a B-line for the empty bar. Sarah Semen's on tonight, so no doubt old J will be flashing his over-hormonal facial growth in her general direction, whilst I set about business: the birth of the NAAC, the Napier Arms Angling Club.

A few days prior, I had been admiring Phil's new koi pond. The work front wasn't what it should be, so I was on the lookout for an earner. Phil's fishpond offered me one on a plate. Whilst watching some pretty impressive fish devour the best part of a whole lettuce, he informed me that those two bigguns are worth over a hundred quid each. Fuck me, I thought, there must be a monkey's worth of carp in there. A potential gold mine in the back gardens of East London, an untapped resource waiting to be harvested. Well, after picking Phil's brains, it turned out there were quite a considerable number of serious fish keepers, part of a club that was run out of the local aquatic shop, who, as it happened, dabbled in the darker side of fish keeping. There was quite a healthy black market in Shubunkin.

The Rabbi, he had pond of sorts – well, a fishless hole in the ground with a few empty Stella cans floating about. Perfect. He could join the local koi club and acquire a list of members, and more importantly their addresses. His posh whistle and nice motor wouldn't arouse any suspicion. Though he didn't need the money, he lived for the thrill of the scam.

Danny, getaway man, driver and generally good for morale. He didn't really mind what we got up to as long as he'd a ten bag in it. Jeff – well, he'd find a way to wriggle out of getting his hands dirty but still get a cut. That was Jeff through an though. Jon and Floyd all-round footmen, do just about anything for a few quid.

Myself – well, fishing equipment and mastermind. I mean, what would it take? A few builders' buckets, gaffer tape, pair of folding trout nets and a few loafs of bread, no?

It was simple; gain access to Mr Orna-mental expensive fish-owners' garden, relieve him of few prized specimens and pass 'em on to the moody aquatic shop. I ran the idea past Jeff, Captain Bird's Eye, the day before our planned meet-up. He pointed out that the aggro-to-profit ratio wasn't all that good. Agreed, it was a lot of hassle, but then so was bumping up two pallets of roof tiles. J, the cunt, Mr Restaurant, survived on his tips, saved his wages, and lived with his mum, so what the fuck did he know? I was already best part of two months behind on the rent; I was in to that mean bastard Steve for few hundred, not to mention my fishing syndicate membership which was due. Still, he offered his services, you know, if alibis were needed, or at a stretch his old girl's bathtub.

So, the Rabbi became a very reluctant member of the

Redbridge Fish Keepers Association. With that came a newsletter and a few choice addresses in Chigwell and Loughton. I'd acquired a pair of cheap and cheerful folding trout nets, buckets and tape. Danny, Jon and Floyd were in; we were good to go, with a green light. Mr Aquatic Shop Vince was interested in just about anything that swam, and I mean anything.

With a loaded gun, the promise of an earner, I went over to Mike and Laura's to score, always good for tick. The smell of ant powder and the sight of dirty needles were starting to make me queezy. Millbrook estate just happened to back onto the Eagle pond, home of the cockney king carp; he held court behind the barbed wire fence, decorated in snagged-up carp rigs you cast from the bus stop. Broken dreams, he was the fish equivalent of Mick O'Malley, a horrible cunt who filmed his own exploits, wanking off to rape and AGBH. The cockney king carp fractured the heads of men, broke up happy homes and enjoyed it, a mean bastard, he took it, he gave it, he fucking loved it.

I lay in the long un-mowed marginal grass and let the cool breeze massage my face. Grey shapes appeared silhouetted behind a Canadian backdrop; marble submariners, wise and portly, they cruised the margins as if they understood a cease-fire was in effect. Forgetting to breathe I lurched and threw up; his lordship never showed, but I doubt very much he'd retired to Canvey.

Walking to the tube I thought of fucking off the rest of them, nicking Phil's fish and selling them to get a nice pair of handmade Avons, filthiest fishing rods around, but my diamorphine-fuelled tackle daydream was interrupted in the form of a London Transport conductor, a little black guy coming like a seventies gollywog, a vicious-looking one in box-fresh Nikes, not at all like the little fellow you would be happy to finding on your jar of Golden Shred:

'Can I see your ticket, sir?'

I just clippered a Marlboro light, and pushed back through

a wall of the well-groomed. I decided on taking the bus.

Two days later I'm sitting next to Danny in some kind of bucket seat, flying up the Epping New Road in this pocket-rocket of a car, at somewhere between the speed limit and the emergency room. I cast a glance as the Wake Valley Ponds immediately become a blur. Not really for me, the whole speed thing, but it floats Dan's boat so what the hell. Jon and Floyd just chuckle like adolescent hyenas. The word fiasco comes to mind as Dan springs open the glove compartment to reveal a roll of foil. Fuck it…

The next thing I know, me and Jon are gouching out, stumbling about in some minted wanker's back garden with trout nets and buckets at the ready. Like a pair of drug-crazed garden knobs, staggering through neat shrub-lined borders looking for a fucking Koi pond. I'd chosen to leave Floyd behind in light of his recent discussion with God. First hit, well, we end up with three goldfish, muddy trainers, and somewhat worse-for-wear upholstery. Dan's itching and scratching like a bitch, not really conducive to high-speed road travel in what amounted to a Coke can on wheels.

'So how's your sister then, Jon?'

That was the final nail in Dan's coffin. His patience evaporated. On our way back we made one last stop by an easy-to-hit detached place in Woodford Green – at the very least I wanted to weigh up Dan for petrol and see everyone right for a lick of gear. I took the initiative as Jon and Floyd were getting pepped to pebble-dash Dan's tacky interior. I wandered around in this nicely kept back garden with a fag in my mouth, unafraid, brandishing a trout net and plasterer's bucket. Once I located the pond, I stabbed about until something was flopping about in my net. I'd had enough. On our way back to the Stow I peered down in the bucket, a plump little common carp, and a pang of nostalgia. I got Dan to stop by the pond on the green. I planted a seed for another generation of camp-bed nippers, or Canvey carp rustlers. She swam from my fingers, ready for us all.

Pond Life 2

The Oak Hill ponds were only a few hundred metres inside of Epping Forest, both a good thing and a bad thing. Just enough to take you to another world, away from the humdrum, but maybe too isolated for a twelve-year-old with a roach pole and pint of maggots. The bigger of the ponds was chocked with reeds but deeper. It held a few surprises. I remember standing there up to my knees in silt and stagnant water, slowly edging through the weed, dangerously over-stretched trying to reach an opening in the reeds without getting caught up in the low-flying perennials.

The float dipped and lifted in a mass of pinhead bubbles and the breeze muffled out the approaching danger. I was busy daydreaming of monster eels. Julian and I had rescued and released some pie-shop victims on a No. 11 recky in to Calcutta, well Eastham, the year before. Three reflections were cast across the water. Four grinning faces clutching buckets and poles; the lads, shit, off the estate. You guessed it: yet another restocking yarn, my first. And to cut a long story short I ended up waist-deep heading a human food chain. One mean bastard Dean with dry feet holding the bucket, followed by the pecking order, the hierarchy of scallywags. The guy behind an even bigger wanker than me, as he was at least the same age as the ringleader, sixteen or thereabouts.

With my somewhat extended reach I managed to fill Dean's bucket up in no time. Impressed by my tench-slaying prowess, I got promoted to gang mascot and invited on several all-nighters over the 'hallowed hollows'. The Hollow Ponds at Whips Cross, a mysterious place for me, like a moonscape due to sandy soil and gravel bank-side. I'd heard of a huge one-eyed pike that used attack small dogs. Straggling ducklings were regularly seen being picked off. It was said Nelson the pike got his eye pecked out by seagull. Or he survived a springtime pikie's harpoon. I never saw any pike landed during my time at the Hollows, but I did see some glorious tench. Their shiny olive green flanks accentuated by the sandy, golden bank-side. They were few and far between; between masturbation contests and practical jokes. But Dean took me under his wing, so I never felt the brunt of that, or had to fill up half a Kinder Egg.

◆ ◆ ◆

I meant to talk about Danny, because he's been dead ten years. I can still hear him give his wisdom: 'There's two kinds of people in this world. There's pricks and there's cunts. You're either one or the other; it's up to you…' It made me wonder what I was, what kind of kid I'd been. I never made it to Dan's funeral. I had already moved abroad by then. Jon had got himself banged up. Floyd had gone loopy, fucking sectioned by his mother. Jeff was last seen hair thinning, donning a beer belly, wandering around Homebase with some tart, fucking liberal, teacher type no doubt, trolley full of pot plants and Polyfilla, poor bastard. The Rabbi had bought a fucking big gaff in the country. Danny had taken a bank loan, became a dealer, got hold of some real choice gear as it happened. Last I saw of him he was giving me the 'pricks and cunts' speech as he passed out in a pool of warm beer. I had to get out; I had to come up for air.

The clincher wasn't long coming. One night I'm woken by what sounded like a dead body being dragged up the bare boards. The carpet had fucked off shortly after Miranda. Since then, Forest Road had become a den of criminal anarchy. As I sat up in bed I heard that nasty bastard Mark outside the bedroom door, another thud with narcissistic giggling. I lit up a Marlboro Light, took a long hard pull, wrapped the duvet round my waist and went so see what the cat had dragged in.

My brother Mark and Terry were dragging a container-load of Hilti drills, compressors and assorted implements up on the landing. They were both bug-eyed; the look on Tell's ashen face said it all. Now Terry was the real-deal wide-boy, for want of a better word. He came from Canning Town, unlike my suburb-raised coward of a brother. Terry, on the other hand, was a truly hard bastard, not a talker; he scared the shit out of me. You have your steamers, talkers and then your fighters. Tell was the latter. A knockout merchant with knuckles so deformed his fist was like bone club.

I witnessed him destroy a pair of big Jamaicans outside McDonalds in Leytonstone once. Now most medium-size white guys tend to smile or look away when two extra-large men of African descent come up on the radar. Not Tell. He gets eye contact. If the big black guys look away or politely smile, all's peachy-creamy. But if the big black guys say:

'Cha man! Blad clat. Bati boy, you wanna step round the back?'

'Naa! You're alright,' says Tell, bold as brass. 'Right here will do.'

There's a sound like meat tenderiser hitting beef, a blink of an eye there's two huge black guys sprawled out on the pavement, headphones hanging round their necks, rolling about in the remains of a Happy Meal. I had to stop him going for the wheel brace. They already needed their jaws wiring. This was Terry. He once bent the rod rings of a beautiful handmade *Seer* rod as it poked from between the front seats. I caught him in the mirror flexing them back and forth. Not a decent bone in the boy.

'Alright Billy Boy,' he said. 'My life, you won't fucking believe this little lot. Your governors gotta want a few of them Hiltis.'

'I don't know, Tell, we ain't had much work lately. It's only just picked up. I'm off fishing in the morning, as it happens.'

As soon as the word fishing rolled off my tongue I knew I had made a huge mistake. I could have said sign on, or even going to visit my mother in her new place. The reply came with lightning speed.

'I'm well up for spot of fishing, Willy, what time we leaving?'

My heart sank. Involving Terry always ended up twisted. The man's newly acquired taste for heroin was not helping the situation. It pacified him half the time, but for the rest he was like a one-man crime wave. Still, he hadn't hit anyone since his new vocation in life as a smack head.

'Alright Tell, what is it now, a quarter to two … how about you meet me outside Threshers at about six-thirty?'

'Sweet, Willy boy! M, you coming?'

Mark threw me a glance like a wounded puppy. Talk about a rock and a shit place. He had been Terry's bitch on the night shift and he knew I wasn't happy about the impending outing. I never did anything with my brother – well, half-brother – we never really got on. It wasn't really surprising when you think it was him graced us with Tony in the first place. Still, he paid the rent on time.

'No, you're alright. I got to dot on in the morning, Tell.'

Wanker, I thought. Still, without old Mark about, Tony would drop the bravado. I declined the chance to have a smoke and went back to sleep.

'Don't be late, Tell, early start in the morning.'

Once awake and laced with Nescafé and a few tugs of Marlboro, I retrieved my fishing bag from behind the water tank. For the life of me I couldn't decide what gear I could lend Terry for the day. The thought of his bony clubs handling my exquisite fishing tackle sickened me. I should have got one of those cheapo telescopic jobbies for such occasions. But with any luck he wouldn't turn up. Wishful thinking. I heard a cough from my brother's room, followed by the sound of someone falling over what could only be a crate of power tools. He hadn't gone home to Vicky, the bastard. There was no way out now. The taxis were starting to add up so the lift would be a help on the wallet unless we got pulled over en route.

He dropped a trail of fag-ash all the way to the toilet and took a piss with the door open. I was preparing bait, chopping up luncheon meat into random shapes, thoughts miles away, seeing a fiery orange float tip sail away in the murky depths of some picturesque little pool when I heard:

'You got any foil at home, Willy?'

'Na, sorry. Sure you should be fucking around with that now, Tell? We got a fair way to go.'

I lied of course. The dirty bastard always dribbled on the floor, never toilet-trained. He mumbled something about the 24-hour garage and flushed. I opened up three tins of sweet-corn, bagged it up and went outside to see what the weather was doing.

I had planned a morning on a lake run by a very strict syndicate, not the place to turn up with your very own psychopath, especially as I only had a kind of guest-ticket situation going on. I was on the list for a permanent place once the time arose. Instead, I decided to have the morning on a small farm pond on the Sewarstone Road, five quid for a day's pasty-bashing. Old Tell would be right at home there, maybe even bump into one of his extended family. It seemed we couldn't go anywhere without some cousin of a long-lost relative crawling out the wood work. Maybe even the pikey farmer was a distant relation.

I walked over to the garage in the glow of the streetlight, opened the big heavy doors. The screwdriver marks in the paint reminded me I had to think about alternative tackle storage. I took down a length of pipe from the rafters, slid out a bundle of rods, laid them carefully on my grandfather's bench. I wouldn't take any of the good ones. I went for a nice old through-action and an old Daiwa spinning rod, both nine foot and unbreakable, suitable for today's experience. I brushed the sawdust off the others and returned them to their secret home.

We loaded up the Ford Fiesta and went shooting off to the local all-nighter. I waited in the car as Terry nicked a few Ribenas and bought a roll of foil. I eyed up a couple of dirty stop-outs as they waddled past the car in shoes that made them look more like pantomime ducks than girls. Once back in the car Tell's nicotine-stained club clutched an unlit Benson, and his head went back and forth like them plastic dogs you see on the parcel shelves of Rover's or Granada's, all to the sound of some fucking horrible shit him and my brother listened to.

'So then, Willy, what we after? How about that place in

Waltham Abbey? They got a right nice little café there; lovely little bird, tits like fried eggs, and the fucking ass on her!'

'I thought we'd give the farm lakes up Sewarstone a try.'

Just the thought of him giving it the biggun in a café full of regulars sent a shiver down my spine. It was chilly but I wound down the window regardless as Tell lit up. What was this shit banging on the stereo?

'Ok Willy, big Willy styles. Left at the roundabout?'

'Yeah, then it's straight through, just do a right at the King George.'

Thing was, Terry actually drove like a car thief. Don't even think he had a licence. If he did it was more than likely moody, you know the deal, belonged to some dead guy from Brussels or fuck knows where.

The gears crunched horrendously as we went catapulting off in the general direction. I looked out the window on my left side; saw a guy getting in his plumber's van, early start before a day's graft. I cast a thought for the chap who'd lost a good few hundred quid's worth of power tools last night. I could accept it on some kind of level; the guy would get a nice claim on the insurance and have few days home with the kids. He'd more than likely pulled a few fast ones from time to time himself, went with the job I supposed. No doubt he would buy stolen gear if approached; who wouldn't?

My mind skipped and danced as we shot past line after line of semi-detached double-glazed shit-holes. Garden gnomes, crazy paving and half-dead hanging baskets all hid their multitude of secrets and lies. Like my governor's habit of going through the underwear drawers of the women we worked for. Even roofers needed access to the house from time to time. So once off to work he never wasted any time getting in amongst it. Toys were like the Holy fucking Grail, I've never seen a grown man look so happy. If he found a double dong he would be beside himself with the possibility it posed, the dirty knicker-sniffer.

His cousin, my work partner, wasn't much better. That time he got a blow-job off that window-licker in Slough always turned my stomach. A good-looking guy as well. Talking of guts, he had this chronic gut problem from too many painkillers, back trouble you know, carrying tiles up ladders for twenty years has its price. He had these shit attacks regularly when he wouldn't have the time to get down the ladder. Real tortoise head touching cloth situations. He must have left more shit under people's lagging than I've had tasty fish dinners. I looked over to Terry. Beads of sweat were forming on his brow. Wouldn't be long now, I thought.

We turned in by the farm. A short dirt track led past some stables, down to the lake. There were already a few cars there. The mist was rolling across the water like a film-set swamp. As we approached the water and pulled over bank-side I saw a few fish rolling. With any luck Tell would be quietly gouching in the back seat, leaving me to concentrate on snaring a few of the lake's carp, getting a bend in my rod before numb-nut's mind turned to knocking out his night's work.

The reeds to my right were getting buffered and shaken. I scanned the lake for any signs of bigger fish, but apart from the rather theatrical mist and odd rolling carp it was pretty quiet.

Just one lone pensioner huddled under a damp umbrella, and a hundred yards to his right two tents, a smouldering fire surrounded by a mass of empty beer cans and other nondescript litter. Nice. Really contributed to the overall atmos.

I dropped a free-lined bait against the wood, a few feet away from the gang of marauding adolescent carp. I closed the bail arm, loosened the clutch and sat back. I heard Terry rustling about. I was certain the lake rules said nothing about the use of hard drugs; as long as you took your own rubbish home and used barbless hooks it should be OK. The line twitched, the slack between the rod rings raised and fell slightly, my racing heart warmed my cold hands as I waited expectantly for a full-blown run. The moment was rudely interrupted:

'Willy, you want a go on this, mate?'

'Was that the gear you got off Dan?'

'Yeah, fucking blinding!'

'Na, not for me, Tell, I'm trying to keep away from that these days.'

'Big Willy! Da fisha man, eh.'

'Yeah, whatever.'

A reply like that could only be considered when he was well pacified. He slammed the car door, sending the breakfasting shoal of carp packing. He wound down the window, the sickly-sweet smell of burning baby formula and heroin wafted down from the car, mingled with the damp grass and sweetcorn, making me retch. It reminded me of a time I wished to forget. How long would it be before they started mainlining? With their lack of character they would fall for sure, I'd seen it so many times before.

The line twitched again and was followed by a steady pull. I struck into a chubby mirror carp. It darted off into open water, and then, as if it knew the drill, it rolled over and considered defeat. Fuck me, even the carp are lacking character these days. It looked helpless in the landing net, a Mark carp for sure, swimming around in a shit-hole, a shit-hole I just happened to share.

An underlying tension was building up as the sun rose. The bites dwindled off. It became a little uncomfortable. Sun in my eyes, I was left wishing I'd had more than Marlboro Lights for breakfast.

A car pulled over by the large oak tree in the area reserved for parking. A young mum hopped out and started helping two young lads with their tackle boxes, packed lunches and whatnot. I knew what was going happen next, it didn't take a rocket scientist. They wouldn't want to get too close to the hung-over-something-rotten brigade in the tents, or for that matter the old boy hunched with a fag in his mouth looking rather unsavoury himself. Having not seen my gouching psychopath side-kick, they would no doubt come and plonk down in my vicinity.

She must have been in her early thirties, slim, unattractive, mouth like a cat's arse, lips pursed hard to show that she didn't particularly want to have anything to do with this lark. No doubt the old man had fucked off, leaving her to do the boy things. The ginger one was hers for sure, the other a mate. They came up between the car and this fishing stage. I looked around and smiled. Talk about a bulldog chewing a wasp; she looked contorted, poor cow. One of the lads, ginger nut, sparked up some conversation.

'Alright mate, caught anything?'

I just got a 'yeah' in when the car door flew open and there was Terry hanging out, doing a first-class impression of cat with a huge fur-ball. You have never seen anything like it. There was this yellow putrid goo coming out of his mouth. The woman recoiled so much she looked as if she owned four chins. The two boys looked decidedly frightened.

'He's not very well, been on the piss all night, love.' What else could I have said?

Something caught my eye; line was pouring from the reel. In the ensuing chaos I sent a small common carp airborne. Unceremoniously, I swung the poor blighter into the wooden stage. Terry was convulsing horribly; our group of accidental onlookers melted off at considerable speed, back towards the safety of their Renault Clio. I brushed the grit off the fish and returned it none the worse for wear.

Terry was coughing his left lung up: the old boy had packed in. And fast approaching from the east was Farmer Giles in an almost fluorescent shell training suit, his dirty bum-bag full of coppers. I'm going to get my hook checked, ten fleeced for a fiver. He stuck out like a sore thumb, not your twill-clad, Barbour-jacket, creep-up-from-behind-some-vegetation-with-a-spaniel type. We were still in London E4. The fan belt slipped all the way home.

Brass Carp

She chops me a line out, then wanders away to fetch a bundle of clean towels. I take my jeans off, roll up a score, take a dap; content, I finish off the rest. Pete runs two little concerns, both cater to my inner compulsions: fucking and fishing.

I'm one of the last evening punters. Svetlana takes her time; she knows I'm one of Pete's mates so I'm not hurried. Instead I lay back and listen to her mutter obscenities in Russian as she rocks gently back and forth. I met Pete on a roofing job over in Kentish Town a few months back now; he was in the scaffolding game as well as having fingers in the massage parlour pie. One thing had led to another, and before I knew it I was giving him a price for some guttering work on his place, a fucking massive drum up near Stansted.

Whilst weighing up the work I couldn't help noticing the unmistakable smell of lake. It had followed me round the gaff with this horny Doberman which Pete had insisted was a harmless, soppy creature. It shit me up nonetheless, horrible thing, with its fucking lipstick hanging out. You didn't know if it wanted to eat you or fuck you. I went up on the flat roof at the back and took a dirty old tennis ball out of an old iron hopper and threw it down for the dog. As my eyes tracked it down the garden I caught a glimpse, a sparkle through the trees.

Svetlana lifts herself off and turns around facing the door and lowers herself back down. I couldn't see much from the flat roof, but, like all anglers, that have-to-investigate-water urge was strong. I finished weighing up the materials and went off for a wander with the Doberman in tow. Svetlana cups my bollocks and quickens tempo.

The lake looked disappointingly small, but as I rounded a corner I noticed this was only the shallow bay of a most enchanting lake hidden from the house, hidden from the world. It had it all. As I surveyed the place, the dog ran off back towards the house; no doubt someone arriving or leaving.

I got that sudden shit-attack feeling you get when you're not supposed to be where you are, jogged a few paces, and jumped in fright. I must have disturbed a group of feeding fish. A splash and boil, three bow waves shot out into open water leaving me unnerved yet dying to get a line wet.

I got the job after giving Pete a rather keen introductory price on the off-chance he'd put some more work my way. Yeah, a little trickled in and I was duly invited to Thursday night card games where, over a few light ales, I picked his brains about the back-garden pond life. I tap Svetlana on the arse and get her to bend over by the table. A glass bowl of Johnnys rattle, shunt dangerously close to the edge while I bang the grandma out of grandma.

It turned out Pete didn't have a clue about the lake or its inhabitants. The house wasn't that old but the lake had been part of an older estate that had long been chopped up and developed after the war. Pete, not being an angler himself, hadn't understood the potential; well, not from a piscatorial angle at least. He told me to talk with Roy, an old boy who fished the lake from time to time, as well as doing a spot of gardening for Pete's old women. As luck would have it old Roy was on the phone. I back out, wiped my cock off and chop out another line.

I spent an hour on dog; Roy filled my head with tale after tale of monster carp, accounts of specimen tench and roach. The place sounded like an angling goldmine, a far cry from the fiver-a-day shit-holes I frequented. Pete had said pop over when you like, please yourself. It was late July and I planned my first visit. Roy tipped me off; floating crust between the boat house and stone wall, said you wouldn't get a take in open water. Cast the bread on the pads. The carp would come up and nudge the bread off, watch it, then suck in once it was water logged and almost sinking. This fucking gear is blinding. I lay back and drape a towel over my stomach. Svetlana reaches for the oil.

I pulled up on Pete's drive late afternoon. Stalking outfit in hand I calmly as possible made my way on foot though the garden, into the undergrowth towards the lake. As the barking died off and the sound of the countryside took over I pushed myself round to the boat house leaving magic beans here and there in likely looking spots. There were dark shapes moving about in the shady island margin, hard to make out as they shifted under the reflection. I grip the side of the bed, concentrating on the paisley-come-puke lampshade. Fucking hums something rotten here; cucumber, baby oil and foot sweat.

There was no sign of anyone having fished it recently. The grass was long, the margins choked. I patted the grass down with my net, baited up, flicked a fifty pence-sized piece of crust on the pads and laid back, switched the check on and lit a fag. There was the occasional slurp or violent shake in the pads, just enough to fuel the imagination and keep me from moving on. My bait just sat there like a crouton in the afternoon sun. Right on the point of giving her a pearl necklace, there's a right going on in the hall outside the door.

I was picking bogies, adjusting my seating and considering a move when my bait was nudged. Like a million volts or amped on stone, as carpio started playing flipper. I sat up, brushed the hair from my eyes and picked up the rod. During the tense wait I thought of bridging the island and cutting out swim on the point. It would only need me to lay my double twenties over the gap. I can hear all sorts outside, radio static followed by shouting in Russian; old Svet wipes her hands on a towel and gestures for me to get my clobber on. I lick the wrap clean and stuff it behind the radiator.

Slowly, over ten long minutes, my bread got edged off the lily pad. It was bobbing about on the far side, rotating slightly as the line uncoiled. It was only a matter of time now before the inevitable … disappointment. The bread sank, the hook pulled free and I was left winding in a slack line as some overly intelligent fish devoured the remains of my waterlogged crouton. I jar open the sash window and bits of mildewed wood fall like helicopter seeds as I shimmy the old cast iron stench pipe, hop the back fence and make my way over the marshes. Have to go back for the van later.

I continued to blank up at the lake until late autumn. Roy's son Dean was over there one afternoon with real carp gear. Turned out Roy had died not long after his conversation with me. It also came to my attention Roy had never actually managed to hook and land any of the lake's carp in all his years, the old charlatan. Talk about a cock and ball. I'm standing there when Dean's banger shot up and the Delkim whined. Bastard! After a short scrap Dean landed a fine torpedo common carp; took a home made boilie in a hole in the weed. Pete got birded up over in West London for year or so. I winkled out my first double on a float-fished peanut, the very evening Pete's missus had me look at her plumbing.

David Knowles

David Knowles went to boarding school in heaven – which is situated in South Wales at the double confluence of the rivers Wye, Monnow and Troddi. Within three miles of Latin classes were at least thirteen species of fresh-water fish, from salmon and shad to grayling and gudgeon. After a quarter-century digression via the cockpit of a Tornado, David is now back in heaven. Which has moved to Loch Broom near Ullapool. Within three or four miles of the Two Ravens Press global headquarters where he lives and works are probably only four freshwater species – but one of them is the sea trout. That is more than sufficient.

David is a writer of short prose and poetry – his first collection *Meeting the Jet Man* (Two Ravens Press, 2008) was shortlisted for the 2009 Scottish Arts Council First Book of the Year Award.

Fish Running

A long shot; the camera is clearly airborne. A single distant figure runs as if possessed in a vastness of wild, deforested landscape. The patchy heather has already turned. From a distance it appears that he carries some sort of weapon: a long spear, or maybe a hunting rifle in a canvas bag. The shot draws in a little and you look for the tell-tale winds of helicopter downwash to give the game away. But there are none. These pictures are from a near-silent drone, covertly holding a kilometre or more away from the subject.

Do NOT for a split second distract me. One false move and I will snap my leg like a Bic biro and that will be the end of it. Check-mate in four. You have no idea. You think it is about willpower. It has nothing to do with willpower. It is a simple matter of sufficient calories. Out here, beyond your bloody 'willpower'. The straight-talking mathematics of exhaustion. No, I can't 'take it easy'. There isn't time, and anyway, it would be counter-productive to go at a 'brisk walking pace' over ground like this. I, you, anyone – we all have to travel fast to counteract the useless bog-squelches that provide no thrust by blending them with the good contacts of sole on solid ground – hard rock if you can find it. Below this speed the image of motion pixelates and we will come to a grinding halt, sink into the black treacle of thousands of years of sphagnum. No bloody osprey rising from the grasp of water then. No lift-off. Lucky to flap-swim waterlogged ashore. So we must concentrate on speed, gather it, save it from decay so that the movement hides the pixels like a television screen. And that takes calories. But I can't talk now. The slope steepens here.

He is running almost exactly along the western edge of the Moine Thrust Belt, the geological flood of Moine Schist that inched and ground its way westwards over Sutherland around 430 million years ago. The Moine Thrusts didn't create this landscape. The rocks of the Moine weren't even thought of when the basement and covering rocks of west Sutherland were laid down. But the Moine added the twist to the tale. Normally geology operates like any fair-minded company: last in, first out. That would have been dull. All the limestone and later nutrient-rich deposits would have gone back into the sea, leaving only the barren grey hump-backs of Lewisian Gneiss, and their stunted-fish children.

The Moine shuffled the deck. Layers of the cake folded over and back on themselves, faulted and strained. Now we have a mosaic, pockets of richness and water-giants. I could tell you the whole story: about the tectonic powerhouse that drove the Moine Thrusts. But to the Fish Runner the tectonic origins of the Moine happened off that map of his, far to the east. And way, way before the end of the last ice age, when fish life began here again. His eyes would glaze over if you talked to him about what is not on The Map. In any case, he is running strongly today and we really mustn't distract him. Christ, as if we could! Today he might make it all the way to the Keyhole Loch. That would really be something. Tried four times already and didn't get close. It is too early in the day to say. He is still on the first leg of 11.2km to the Bearded Rock, running almost due north, climbing (net) about 800ft on a mix of heather and, increasingly, sphagnum bog. (You'll find details on the web-site, or interactive if you have it.) Of course, the trenches are still ahead on the second and third legs and they are the real obstacle. But still, he certainly is running strongly today.

Long-distance running. Yeah, well – we've all done it. Finding the pace, controlling the breathing, focusing on the cold pain which stays conveniently still – long enough to negotiate with it. Not here. No two paces alike. No paths. Except for a few trace-lines in the rough grasses, made by red deer. Who go where they choose for reasons known only to themselves and which are of no use to me. So the mental techniques are different here. Look well ahead and plan the moves like a draughts player – while not putting your feet in a suck-hole of peat or a bear trap. No, not a figure of speech. They really could trap a bear. Where the peat, maybe twenty-five feet thick in places, has been monstrously undercut by water. Where there is just a tiny hole, hidden by heather, above the blackest of leathery-sided, leg-snapping caves. An organic crevasse. Still, come on: look well ahead and imagine a series of stepping stones over deep water. Some of which are false. Sometimes you have to take a short-term hit to get to the good stuff: the firm ground where a little bedrock shows through. The rush of a gathering sprint for eight painful strides may project you up and out of a gully. Worth pushing the burn in your thighs that far into the red for a few seconds? Maybe. If you pick the right route. And always, when you fall, as you will on occasion today, the rod must be flung clear before you go down. It is lighter than you. It will land soft.

We don't know for sure why he insists on carrying a conventionally sectioned rod. Ten foot six, two sections, ideally an AFTM 7-weight line. I dare say it could take down to a 6-weight. It looks delicate enough. It would even take an 8 without running out of steam until the cast was longer than the Fish Runner generally makes. He fishes close and quiet. But why not a Hardy Smuggler, or a Sage Z-axis? If you are covering a lot of ground like this it would make sense to have both hands free – strap the rod to your back. Me and the rest of the control room boys suspect that it's the expense. Those multi-section rods are pricey, unless you'll settle for something with an action like a football rattle. We reckon he's skint after the best part of two years obsessively working at The Map. Other than that cryptic map, for which he thinks there is no price on earth, his gear is inexpensive. So maybe he just can't afford the Hardy.

You wondering? Why the long rod? Maybe I just don't like the action of the short-section rods. Maybe I'm skint. Whatever you like. I don't have the breath to gasp out a fucking novel. No flashbacks about a career gone down the kazoo. No poorly lit scene of into-the-night research over leather-bound Victorian volumes from second-hand shops – while friends and colleagues agonise over what went wrong. No telling little close-up onto slightly sub-grade fell-running shoes. What? You think I'm wearing factory seconds? No, mate. These are bespoke Walshes. Like ballet shoes with tread. Shoes like these will pull off great, deep gobs of skin within ten miles if you get them wrong. But these are right. And you might imagine it cost a lot to have them made right. Or maybe I have a mate at the factory? Whatever. So let's just say I like toting the long rod, eh? I love the way it flexes with the pace. The tassels of the bag's tie-laces sway with the rhythm. I carry it almost parallel with the ground, arm just off straight. It makes me feel like Daniel Day-Lewis in *Last of the Mohicans* – running easy with his Long Carbine. That rhymes with baked bean, by the way. French.

We like a side-bet, the other lads and me. Not about whether he'll actually crack the big issue: whether he'll decode The Map. Even we wouldn't be *that* flippant. The Map is an article of faith around here. We all stand or fall with The Map. That's the name of the series – The Map. It pays all our wages and plenty besides. But just a little bet sometimes about how far he'll get on the day, whether he'll catch something relevant, fit a piece of the jigsaw. Today has a particular edge – the fifth shot at the Keyhole Loch. The other four attempts will need editing into a single montage of suffering and disappointment. Not too long. Just enough to whet the appetite for eventual success. Keyhole Loch, so-called because of the shape of it: *Loch Toll na h-Iuchrach* in Gaelic. But coincidentally (or maybe not, eh? The Boss doesn't miss a trick) it might be the piece that unlocks The Map. And we all want The Map unlocked. Soon, actually, before the audience concentration span is exhausted. Though we sure as shit don't want to be up there with him. Christ, have you seen the terrain? Look. I'll keep the left screen on him – The Boss would have a melt-down if I left him for a second. But here on the right I'll take a little stroll down the second and third legs. Easy-peasy, wide-angle ... pan it out ... Now, this area that looks like tiger skin. All the way down the valley-side from the rocky escarpment to the boggy mess at the bottom and then most of the way up the other side. Looks almost pretty from back here. Like tiger skin does – cuts in silk. Cuts in flesh, more like. Now let's just ... zoom ... in ... closer. See? Each damned stripe is a peat trench you could lose a car in. And on and on, those tiger stripes, for over a mile and a half.

Bearded Rock. My glacial erratic pit-stop. A bearded boulder friend maybe ten feet on the near-cube. Solid Moine Schist, just plonked here in the middle of the gneiss by a wandering glacier. A giant, with his mates here and there stranded in the middle of post-glacial nowhere – as if waiting for a bus. Now complete with pale green fronds of lichen. Hence the name. This is the first allowable stop. You can't just stop any old place. An unscheduled stop is a little defeat that will almost certainly turn into a rout and failure. This is a planned stop; an entirely different thing. Here there is shelter, whichever way the wind. Get my breath back a bit. Not long. Intake calories. That means 'eat' to you. I don't see it that way. Pre-planned stop. Precise amount to take in. Recovery fast. Five minutes max.

Aye-aye, Fish Runner. Might have a cup of tea myself, since you offer. No, no. I'm only kidding. Of course he can't hear me. But I will put the kettle on. Keep an eye, will you, and shout if anything wacky happens. I'm just round the corner here.

Calories. Carriage-weight versus necessity. Everything as light as possible. Uhh. And taste must weigh extra. I'm like an astronaut out here in empty, cold space. I have only the most fragile and tenuous life-support. Mentally and physically. The calories are a form of advanced survival ration – military specification originally. Mail-order off the net. No goddam picnic hampers here. Not unless you bring them on an argocat.

Some stranger's hands feel over the jerkin that keeps everything tight to my body. They check it every time I stop. It's the drill, I don't even think about it. Stop, unwrap, put in mouth, masticate with the sticky white froth I call saliva. Water if absolutely necessary. Water is heavy. I never carry it. Always suck it through this filter straw. Great invention. Fifteen grammes, this one. Then the ownerless hands run over the known shapes of flybox, spool, priest. I lean back a fraction and feel the end of the short landing net nudge the base of my spine. Well; all's well. A priest? Why the weight of a priest when everything else is cut to the nearest gramme? You know the answer to that: Respect.

Can you imagine if any one thing were missing? Like the time we went to Gilaroo, Alan and me. All the way there and 'Couldn't spare me a length of 5lb, could you, mate? Seem to have left mine in the car.' Fucking idiot. Me, I check and check and check. And there is redundancy. Four flies and a length of nylon sewn into the hood of my running top. I'll never need them. But they are there. The main fly box is in the lower left pocket. I took a set of weighing scales into the tackle shop and shaved twenty-four grammes off my previous box. This one is cosy, sure. Flies right tight up against each other. That could get confusing. Especially now that I'm finally down to only seven patterns, with forty-eight examples of each. Black Pennell, of course. Three sizes of hook, two weights of each hook size, and a light and a heavy dressing on each. Four examples of each specification. Comes to forty-eight. I created a code to make them instantly recognisable. Either four turns of ribbing wire for the light hooks or five for the heavy. An extra turn at the butt for the fuller dressing. Always a double whip-knot to finish and re-varnish the head after two hours. The other patterns? Bibio and Connemara, Olive Bumble and Peacock Spider. That's five. You can guess the rest, I'm sure.

But those bloody argocats. Twice I've tried to get in here and been blocked by some keeper and his stalking party of unfit bastards in an argo. They are a desecration. People who can't at least *walk* in here should not *be* here. Everywhere I go seems dogged by them. You'd be amazed. I keep coming across argocat tracks in places you wouldn't believe. And of course that was the end of it – the fishing party – when they wanted to take an argocat to Gilaroo.

We do our best to be invisible. We have to. The attraction is all in the fact that he doesn't know we are there. Doesn't know he is on television. But of course, where there is big money involved the sponsors like to feel they have their 'finger on the pulse' – what an expression! It seems to have enjoyed a sardonic resurgence round here, reflexive retro-bollocks. And they would want to be out 'on the ground' on just the day when the Fish Runner decides to leap out of bed and head north at two in the morning. Luckily, we had kitted them out to look like a shooting party. And the Fish Runner, of course, does not carry binoculars. But it was a close one. Today the team are miles back and all the remotes are well camouflaged.

Fishing parties – someone should write a book on them. All life is there – the zealots and the enthusiasts, the dilettantes and the organisers. And the busy-bodies. Must have been ten seasons we fished as an identifiable group. Not always at the Altnaharrie Hotel. But mostly.

Altnaharrie was one of a system of Victorian sporting hotels which gave coverage of the whole Highlands. They weren't on holiday. Not those sportsmen. They were gathering the knowledge, bit by bit, which would allow them to map out the connectivity of the fish and the game and the geology. The whole system as a single entity. They needed to know how it worked. The hotels were the far-flung outposts of the knowing-empire. Luxurious in their day. Built to last. Hell, half the furniture is still there. Oversized chairs with arm-rests as thin and transparent as an old woman's skin. Each hotel had leather-bound catch-record books, generally sized at Royal or Cartridge and printed with column headers: weather, height of the water, heaviest fish, total bag ... completed in meticulous detail at the end of each day of the season in the same clerk's perfect calligraphy for year after year. Picture him hovering in the hotel lobby to collect the precious data. Tricky job when some London banker and his mate in shipping have blanked: like having to ask 'So how is your good lady wife today, sir?' and risking the answer 'She died last week.' Yep, tricky questions of etiquette for the catch-book clerk. Then at the end of each week a summary by the head ghillie, as if solemnising the week's work.

One after another the great hotels are folding. Manager-owners come and they hold back the tide of overdue maintenance for a year or two. Maybe they find some other enthusiast to hand the baton to before they are exhausted. But eventually the window frames can't hold another coat of paint over the rotten wood and the building passes into decay – or more likely into private ownership.

Our fishing party had a variable cast. Some years Alan couldn't make it, some years Frank sent his apologies. That other old fart, I forget his name – he was only there for a couple of years and then faded away to bone-fish in the Bahamas. Used to refer to any fish under 2lbs as 'More bait! Ha, ha, ha.' Twat. Then there were a few novitiates who took one look and declined their vows. Me, I never missed a year.

Nobody actually liked anyone else. A few of us grew to really hate each other. Deeply. The party wasn't held together by any friendships – it was far more stable within the mirror-image of friendships, a vitriolic Wonderland. Less loathings compensated for more loathings or something almost chemical like that. It was Geoff and I who started 'The Entwhistle Party', as the hotel staff unfailingly called us. Though of course it was Geoff's friends who provided rank and file. He did have a lot of friends – from television mostly, or the associated baggage train. He hadn't been working specifically on nature programmes when The Entwhistle Party started. But his big break into producing was a piece based around Gilaroo, the year after we first fished it. Not that the party was part of the programme, except for a few miscellaneous shots in the bar one night. Three seconds of fishy fame. No, he'd managed to get that fishing actor bloke – what's-his-fucking-name? – I never watch television so I couldn't care less. Anyhow, this moustachioed wag with a spanking new set of gear turned up on the third day of the week and looked earnestly proud of the two fish that Geoff hung on the end of his line. Amidst the entertaining quips. It was taboo to talk about who had actually hooked the fish. 'That is not the point, gentlemen.'

Geoff made me sit through the video the following year. He knew I wouldn't have seen it so he brought a copy especially for me. Thanks. It seemed to amuse Geoff that I'd rather watch fingernails grow than sit in front of a television, even his bit of television. But amusement wears off. Wore off, the more famous a producer he became. One year I told him straight out. The modern nature documentary is just a piece of shit commodification, the same as everything else on the 'wee screen'. A quick five minutes sitting quietly in your purple Goretex shell and Bingo! – an otter hauls up and has a leisurely breakfast, an osprey has a walk-on part in the background. Then the 'Factfile'. I'll give you the frigging Factfile! 'A great way to see the otter at a range of less than ten metres is to stay at Liam and Anthea's Encounter Centre on the island of not-so-far-away where they moved two years ago after Liam's first nervous breakdown at the advertising agency in which he was an unsuccessful partner. And, by the way – not that you care because you are there for the otters – Liam and Anthea's 'local' chef (he's lived there at least six months longer than they have) was voted best winkle-soufflé-er in the entire Highlands. (By some obscure body of winkle-chefs.)'

There are some things you just can't un-say. We papered over the cracks, even fished together on the final day. But we were looking too hard for pleasant things to say to each other and they all came out flat. At the end of the week we made all the right noises. 'Same again next year?' 'For sure, wouldn't want to let you get ahead.' 'Great, stay in touch.'

Because whatever the fishermen think, a fishing party has a momentum of its own. Who knows if Granddad's Old Axe isn't still chopping away at Altnaharrie. You'll find some parties at the old hotels in the Highlands going on and on for decades. They are always referred to by the original name – 'The Mackenzie Party back again first week in August', or 'The Hogarth Party needs an extra boat this year' – when nobody in the party has that surname and no-one even knows who the original 'owner' of the party used to be. No, I mean that wasn't why I broke away from it and never dreamt of going back, whether The Entwhistle Party continued or not. I finally stomped off because of the fucking argocat. Alan and his fucking argocat. Alan and I never got up the energy to hate each other. I don't hate chicken shit. I just don't ever want to shake hands with it. I was always fast off to the fishing. I didn't used to run when there was company. But you could probably tell I wanted to. So Alan always had his little joke: 'Here comes *The Fish Runner*'. After the book, you know: very well read, is Alan. We tried not to be paired up for the day. A quiet word with the manager normally sorted it when he was working out the roster at the beginning of the week. But by the end of the tenth year he'd have needed a bloody mainframe to juggle all the personal preferences for not spending the day fishing with *him*. Well, Gilaroo was always a challenge for Alan. Sweating his shambling way up the hill. So when the only-best-malt keeper offered him the use of his old argo, he naturally couldn't see any reason not to accept. Over my dead body. And that was the end of me and the fishing party.

It would have ended anyway – when I found The Map. There was no point in pretending any more. I only fished with other people because it allowed me to gather information faster. One man couldn't put the Victorians' jigsaw back together on his own. Not with just odd pieces and guesswork. Too much knowledge lost since the end of the nineteenth century. My belief is that they were close to completion. But most of what they had pieced together had not been written down. At least, it was written in catch records and personal journals, but not collated and published. So the individual insights and breakthroughs remained guesswork on the verge of coalescence. Then the whole fragile matrix was pummelled into the mud of the First World War. Leaving me just glimpses here and there in old hotels and castles, the collective muddled memory of the west-coast Highlands. It seems they never produced the imaginative thinker to bring all the pieces together. At least, it had seemed that way until I found The Map. Thanks, indirectly, to Mr and Mrs Ballantine.

For the last two weeks in August 1882, the Ballantines came to Assynt. Mr and Mrs – and for the next sixteen years without a gap. Then never again. Always two weeks. Either they had no children or the children were born earlier in life and left in Glasgow with a nanny. These scourges of the Loch Assynt Ferox arrived after their luggage, sent on ahead. They brought more than enough of their money from coal to hire the two crofting men needed to row them and their dead-bait herrings around the loch for a fortnight. With a break or two for the fly. The two 6lb-plus fish over the main door of the hotel and the 9½lb cock next to the rod room are theirs. Attributed to Mr and Mrs Ballantine. Not a patronising gender gesture in those days. It was understood that the boat took the fish, not the individual rod. Who knows whether he hooked them, or her. Or the oarsmen. It didn't matter then. Wonderful catches they made, rarely a year without some headline fish. Then, after the trip of 1898, they never came again. Ghillie Mackenzie's close-of-season remarks for that year note only the 'good fortune that a life was not taken by the fishings this year'. The current barman had heard of them but knew nothing more. The manager started well, with a grand gesture introducing The Ballantine Mystery as some sort of party piece – but only knew something vague about a near-drowning and other whispers. Geoff wondered about a documentary – but never followed up on the idea, as far as I know. I didn't think much more about it – there were more promising leads to exploit. Until the following year. When I had a really unbelievable piece of luck. It never would have happened if Geoff hadn't been called away with work at the last minute. He always had the Rowan Room. Every year – said he liked the view. The manager insisted that I take it – best view in the hotel, long-standing customer and all that blah.

I don't ever unpack in hotels. I live out of a holdall. Two, actually. Washing slowly transfers from the clean bag to the dirty bag and then I go home. Chests of drawers have only one part to play in this process. On the last day I have to check that there is nothing in the drawers. Even though I am not a magician and have not performed the trick of putting object into the drawers without ever opening them. Maybe I might have done. And don't you always hope that something valuable will have been left, overlooked in a hotel drawer?

There was the usual yellowed newspaper liner with some really old-looking typeface. I almost closed the drawer again when my eye caught 'Loch Assynt' in the sub-headline. *The Inverness Courier* – dated 28 Aug 1898. The gothic story of a stormy day on Loch Assynt – a deeper trench than anyone dared fathom. A Mr Ballantine of Glasgow had insisted on fishing despite the weather and strong winds. Mrs Ballantine, usually at his side, had refused to leave the hotel on such a day. The boat wrecked on the rocks and the oarsmen, local crofters, were near-exhausted when they got back to the hotel, wide-eyed, having been forced to swim ashore from an island. Mr Ballantine? They shook their heads. Only, next morning, a neighbouring estate's stalker found him wandering near Achfary – fifteen miles away from the loch. And not just any old fifteen miles. Up over the top of the Assynt massif and down the other side – that type of fifteen miles. Very wet, very cold and very incoherent. Theories and rumours abounded. The crofters had tried to rob and murder him. A funnel cloud had sucked him up and deposited him on the far side of the mountain. There was talk of a massive creature that lived in the loch. A lot of talk, except from Mr Ballantine: who never said a word about the affair, stayed locked in his room for two days before leaving the hotel, never to return to Assynt.

And there it was, under the newspaper. The Map. A corner stuck to the resin of the drawer wood, peeled off brittle but undamaged. I just knew its significance immediately. The Map could have been made for me. I had been waiting for it. Laugh all you like, my fingers did tremble, like an old alchemist with gold. The Map is more than a work of art, startling though the illustrations are. It is all at once a cipher, a guess, a signpost. It broadly takes the form of a spiral, driving in towards the central keyhole device. There the words *Toll na h-Iuchrach*, meaning keyhole, but also crux, maybe even solution. I think the draughtsman must have used some optical projection device to preserve the precise but shrinking proportionality as the spiral approaches the centre. That was how global maps were originally made – a light source within a semi-transparent globe, projected on to a cylinder of paper in which the sphere was suspended: The Mercator projection. Because, in spite of its spiral form, I know this is actually a map. It tells us that bodies of water which appear to us to be distant from one another are in fact near neighbours across the spiral. The coils of the spiral are interwoven with beautiful line drawings of fish acting like stitches – to sew their world together.

Aren't they the finest moments? Moments without hesitation. The decision to pursue a line to its furthest limit. As soon as I saw it, I knew that The Map was a life's work. I have the freedom to do that: to swing all my resources behind one obsession. No ties, and I was only keeping you guessing before: I make stacks of money. Half the time I don't know how much. I run internet ordering services for small-to-medium-sized companies. My systems automate the process of ordering, invoicing, follow-up admin. I never even meet my customers any more. Remote automation and remote payment. The servers and the back-ups are my colleagues. Pity they can't fish. Be a sight better company than most of the arseholes I have fished with.

I've never seen the whole map. There has always been a lot of secrecy in the studio. More so, now that the series is a big hit. The Boss must have a copy, of course. The rumour is that some art-forger mate of his from Croydon did the work. He specialised in knock-off original Victorian fishing prints. Big money in fishing antiques these days. No, I've only ever seen bits of The Map at meetings to discuss setting up the next location. It is a great production to be involved in – exciting, because you don't quite know in advance how the Fish Runner is going to turn his way through the maze. And some wonderful opportunities for original camera-work. The episode with the copper fish was my favourite, from a cameraman's point of view.

The Map takes you places. It suggests connections and points you in a direction. It isn't easy to describe without The Map in front of you. Try to picture it like this. You buy an old house. There is a trunk in the attic. A ship in a bottle, bookends with bronze leaping fish. A mottled leather briefcase that should contain papers but is so heavy to lift. Clasps stuck with verdigris, forced open. The gleam, deep down tugging in the less-than-halflight of deep water. A polished copper trout without ornament or stylising. Almost the real thing. Lacquer has kept it untarnished for a century. You so want to know where the fish came from and if there might be a pair, if they might possibly still be caught.

The outline on The Map just had to be the Uists. Not an accurate piece of cartography; distorted out on the rim but recognisable nevertheless, like a face in a crowd. The obelisk symbol next to it, over which a fish leaps, laughing, meant nothing to me. There was only one place to start – The Loch Kildonan Hotel. Part of the old network. The hotel leans, affronted, over the harbour and sniffs as the Oban ferry docks. None of the hotel's rightful clientèle aboard. No servants or luggage trolleys with the local children marching respectfully behind, just in case. One of the last to go under, The Loch Kildonan had hung on grimly through to 1985 on the backs of yacht crews looking for a shower. It crumbled gracefully before finally closing its doors.

Because the caretaker had an interest in local history and I spun him a line about a book I was writing, he let me into the hotel. Through the kitchen: the other doors were too firmly boarded up. The electric was off but enough light came down the stairwell from the atrium. There were still the old stuffed fish, half casts mostly. Gold lettering on the glass. But the catch books were gone and he didn't know where. The most prestigious Outer Isles fishing hotel from halfway through the nineteenth century to just shy of the end of the twentieth – and their records were probably in somebody's 'snug' study with the first edition (unread) Walton, the signed photo of Conrad Voss Bark and probably a singing perch from the guys at the golf club. Fucker.

The caretaker had heard of the copper trout but he didn't know if they had ever been real fish or just a local legend. Searching the islands with nothing but The Map, which he did not need to know about, was not going to cut it. There is a lifetime of fishing water on each the Hebridean islands, Atlantic string vest that they are, and few to guide you through them. On most of the eastern coast the croft houses are long, long deserted and the tracks and the knowledge gone. Everyone knows a man who knows a man who used to know when, on the tide and the moon and the rains, there might be good fish. I pretended only half an interest in the old photo of the brick chimney, maybe 50ft high, still steaming with what I now realise is whale blubber boiling. The chimney is the symbol on the map. The shape, the exact shape that I thought was some sort of glyph. Oh yes, the caretaker knew fine well about the old whaling station. The chimney still stands among the ground-level outlines of the other buildings which were recycled for field walls and '30s houses. He knew a man who knew a man who used to be able to get to the landward side by boat on the loch. But with the sluices in disorder for fifty years the precipitates had built up in the channels. He wasn't sure about a boat now. 'Not to worry – I was just curious.' I set out that night in darkness with the car left miles away as if abandoned outside the hotel bar.

The chimney was perfect for cameras. We had to get a steeplejack in there on the quiet. That was a palaver. Wouldn't do for even the locals to know we had the place wired for surveillance, so not only did we have to pay some rope-access nutters from Glasgow to do the climbing but we had to pay them to keep quiet as well. Whatever the expense, it was worth it. The shots are fabulous. Just high enough to be panoramic but not high enough that you get that awful God's-eye feeling of vertigo and detachment. We knew roughly when he'd appear, and then it was a matter of sit and wait. We might even sell some of the nonspecific footage. We got some great shots of otter. This big old dog-otter on his morning rounds of the inlet next to the factory, sunning himself on the remains of the jetty. Staying seaward of the sluices. Or we might have had to send him on his way. Wouldn't have wanted him interfering with the Fish Runner's copper fish.

The walk-in turns into a trot and *The Long Carbine* spurs me on to the low, loping canter of good ground. Contouring the foothills of Hecla keeps me clear of the bogs and the thickest of the woody heather. I drop down to the water at a neck where three lochs meet. A clachan of lochs. They trade salt for the nutrients of a swan colony, fine silt for fresh water and the promise of spawning burns. The neck is a Zanzibar marketplace of crossing paths. Stood at a single rock I catch a yellow-belly black-spot tiger of a trout and a stubborn, fat pollack of a pound and a quarter. Nymphs of the native dark olive are being hounded by flounder. I move on past bright orange bladderwracks and pale, small sea anemones – but no sign of a tide. Only the age-lines of debris on a loch which rises and falls with the rain, not the moon. The water too salt to drink, but still I catch trout; the loch pressing eastwards and hunkering down between cliffs colonised with small rowans, singing and ringing. The water draws its belly in – to a width of no more than fifty yards. Rounding one last point I see that I must have been fooled onto the wrong arm of water. The channel I have followed is a dead-end: a box canyon of rock that barely sees the sun, that is upholstered with moss. I reach a hand into the water and taste. Salt. Strong salt, a good half seawater. But where is the sea?

Hey, hey, hey. There he is. Look, just coming around the point on the left. We're on. The light is pretty good and we're on! With a bit of luck this'll finish the episode. It was getting tight for the deadline.

I am James Bond discovering the secret underground rocket silo disguised as a volcano. Water is gently flowing through an artificially spaced line of boulders and under the blank end-wall of the loch. Deep, deep in the clear water between the two central blocks a giant forest of weed is cat-stroked by the current. From close above is an echo of waves. I do not know how to fish this place. There is no other place like it in the world. Above the end-wall of the loch, isolated against the sky to the south-east, is the top of a chimney.

Come on, Fish Runner. I can't make footage out of you sitting on your arse looking at the water come and go. We've already wrung out the last drop of interest in the mad whaling station owner who decided to connect Loch Bee to the east coast of the island. With dynamite and pick-axes and men waiting for a fresh whale carcass to work. He had them blast and scrape a trench like a small-gauge railway cutting for a hundred and twenty yards through solid rock. Then installed two great clapper-boarded sluices through the remaining twenty-foot-thick wall. Those guys. They just loved to make connections.

Almost at the second the flow stopped, there was movement in deep water. How do we see it? What do we see? Some filter in the mind suddenly says that one of the fantasies of fish is not a fantasy. Then another. A pale mouth open, or a trick of the fading current? I have no way to get a fly down deep to them except … a sinking braided leader and one or two gently weighted flies. It will not be enough. Before I have thought the problem through, the movement is over. Soon I doubt the memory. The deep weed now lies back into the loch. But what if? What if they have gone out through the cliff to the sea to feed? Are the copper fish a type of slob-trout? But they will have to come back through, sometime in the next four hours. If I hold a fly deep in the landward side of the channel and lift when I see movement...

God damn it. Boss, I know, I know. I can see he has a big fish on. I just don't have the light levels to get any more resolution. We can get the footage of him playing the fish at dusk and that's about it. Oh Jesus, come on, Fish Runner. At this rate it'll be too dark to get any sort of shot by the time he lands it. That fish is going like a train. Did you see the thing, when it jumped the first time? Was that a trout or something else? Me neither. Well, look. If the worst comes to the worst we can splice in some footage of a fish from some other place. Fiddle around with the colour a bit and Bob's your copper uncle.

Beware, the next two legs to Keyhole Loch are an agony. I say two legs, because somewhere in this sump of a glen we must stop and eat something. Check the gear – though we wish not to. Only, there is nowhere specific to stop. Which is to say everywhere could be a stop and that means every moment one might stop and so, in every moment, stopping has to be resisted close up, eye to eye. You may wish to reconsider. We are going into the trenches. We will descend, net, maybe fifty feet, then climb back again. But to do that we will crawl and slither and punch our way up and down a thousand foot of exposed peat. We cannot see ahead, we can barely stay upright on the sloping black ice. I don't know how you will cope. I keep the pace with fear. Fear is a good runner. What is there to be frightened of? Stags bellowing in the mist burning off the glen walls? Spooky, I'll grant you. But no, what is really frightening is ... that bloody thing down there. The sucking sublime that mirrors the lonely mind. Oh, that bloody loch that scares the hell. Just to look at it. Enough even not to look at it but just to know it is there. That patch of sky-brightness on a dull day, catching some unnaturally green weed-stalks mutated from the craven blackness of the water. Their roots in an unstitched loll of peat-flesh forming a shallow ridge almost to the centre. Never trust shallow water surrounded on three sides by deeps: a long walk to the gallows, salivating peat all around you.

See how the whole glen seems to radiate like spokes out from the loch? That's because the whole glen is a magician's silk handkerchief being drawn into the clenched fist of the water. But no wrist. No outflow burn. The water, the peat, everything goes down the plughole of that damned loch and does not reappear. Even the burn that runs in, down the steep slope I must shortly climb, is trapped and its head held under. The burn sees it too late. It would run back up the hill if it could, but water crowds forward on water and tramples itself in the rush. Only there, where the burn enters, might you stand at the side of this loch. On a tiny isthmus of heather and rushes with a few stones at the burn's mouth kept clear of the encroaching peat by the current. Surrounded by ten acres of active sump-oil, actively plotting to preserve the image of you in weak acids. There one *might* stand and cast a line. Nowhere else. Go within thirty yards of the water's edge – moot point, the water's edge – and there would be swift, sinking justice meted out to you. Black cloth on your head. But there – there on that isthmus one might stand and cast a line in a nightmare. If you approached under the protection of the burn. God help them if there are fish in that lattice of suspended water-soot. God help you if you caught one and heard the gnashing of big-head-almost-no-body jaws that scrape over each other like dagging shears. No, best not even to look at this far blacker than *dubh* loch. You might carelessly imagine casting line here or there. Just hypothetically standing at that water's edge, impossible though it clearly is, might be enough for the peat to gain a gum-hold. Then slowly, slowly quick-fatal.

The rest of the peat is dull. We'll have to edit most of it. Leave a shot of him sprawling flat on his face, one of him clawing his way out of a rut too deep to jump or power out of. I'll get the shots and then just pan out and take a breather. It's still two hours to the end of my shift.

One of the technical problems of putting the programme together is that we don't get much of a soundtrack. The cameras were put there by helo or the keeper took the crew in with the argocat. Microphones, being much shorter range, are trickier. Though he does talk to himself the whole time. So we have to cut in a load of stuff – you know, factfiles on Victorians in Uist, Ferox fishing in Assynt. I find that pretty interesting, mind. Though I could care less about fish. Geology is my bag. It all comes from hunting for garnets on Scourie beach when I was a kid. You never forget that *Journey to the Centre of the Earth* feeling.

Well, that's the trenches done with. Now he has a steep climb alongside the Fairy Burn. This bit is really steep all the way for about eight hundred feet. We reckon that if he isn't at the top of the Fairy Burn by 11 o'clock then he'll need to abort. The remaining distance is relatively short but he has to be back out before nightfall. He doesn't have the kit to survive. We really aren't talking about uncomfortable here. We are talking serious danger. Not that we know what he thinks the cut-off is. None of us have ever spoken to him – except the Boss, of course, but that was when they were mates, a few years ago. And the Fish Runner does pull off some surprises – even to us, let alone the audience. I guess that's why he's so popular. Even now, anaesthetised as they are, the audience still seems able to smell the real thing.

Words hard here fragments in the thick mist of lungs heart pushing to the top. Glimpse with salt-sting eyes, even in the rain, or was it a memory in sunshine of a tiny patch of Japanese garden in the burn, a pool three feet across, laid out and with fish quietly the size of cricket bats. Only ... I see the bottom and must push on.

Jesus, but he's going for it today. He couldn't possibly run all the way up the Fairy Burn – half of it counts as tough scrambling. Nobody could. But he pushes and powers up the way on all fours then grabs six paces at the run when there's a flat. Heaving breath I can see from here, like an accordion. Never seen him quite like that. Can't be good. But he's made a bit of time.

Sorry, went into gabble a bit there, eh? Brain starts to break down when the blood chemistry is so far off. Recover fast now we are at the top. Dizzy stop eat. Just had to be done. Sorry. I know it really hurt deep hands cut. But that was the crux move. The trial. The initiation. Somewhere in that prostration we became higher than the Keyhole Loch. We will soon descend to *Toll na h-Iuchrach*! Joy. Elation. Sorry, I hate to hurt you like that. Stop, recover, eat.

Keyhole lies in the far lobe of a double-lobe glacial corrie on the rim of which the Fish Runner now stands as if ready to base-jump. A lovely shot. For the first time we can see where the sea would be to the north on a clearer day. Fine drizzle is falling now and wrappings of nimbostratus form and decay on upslopes. Way, way below the corrie is the valley leading out to the north. Mile after mile of moraine trash. Then no road in sight until the coast. You see why he had to face the trenches. No other route in.

Just here is the furthest I got in all the previous attempts. This far and exhausted. Knowing I'd have to spend the night if I pressed on. Like now. Chances are that the night wouldn't kill me. Though there is no cover, no fuel and you can get hailed on in July up here. You could be in really serious bother after a day's running. But it isn't that. It's facing the night on my own. The questions, always the same questions that have an answer in the day but overrun me at night. How lonely is a belief that none share?

Today I have one secret weapon. Nobody saw me do it. I made sure of that. Last time I was here, played out, I lay half under the shelter of this slab boulder I'm leaning on now and I slid about four hundred calories, vacuum-packed, into a dry recess under the rock. Nobody knows I put them there and nobody sees me retrieve them today. Now, down into the corrie.

Well, bugger me if he hasn't made it. Ladies and gentlemen – the shores of Keyhole Loch. But late in the day, way late. The ratings will be great when this airs. I'm staying past shift. He does this. Look. Before he puts a line in the water he kneels. Thought he was praying for a while. God, we'd have to edit that out. Now we aren't sure. Seems more like he's looking at the plants. Way to go, Fish Runner. All that way and still the energy to press some flowers.

It is in the rocks. The answer to all your questions. All life, right up the chain to the fish. Quite literally, their life-blood flows out of the rocks. I catch my breath, such little as there is of it, when I see the tiny white flowers. Here, in this small depression leading up and away from the water: Limestone Bedstraw, *Galium sterneri*. At this altitude! Surrounded for miles by nothing but deergrass, star sedge and spike-rushes. Impossible. *Galium sterneri* can only grow in base-rich soils. The whole landscape turns on this tiny flower. The towering sides of the corrie peer over at it and know that they are pivoted around its presence. The flower blinks in the breeze and shyly acknowledges their pledge of allegiance. You young prince. I already know you from another loch: Loch Urigill. A loch of the golden plover and the greenshank, of blanket bog, cotton-grass and sundew. Except in a small bay known locally as the White Shore, where a long-forgotten fault-line has held a tiny piece of the Urigill limestone hidden under the carpet. The erosion missed it; a calcium-rich piece of dirt left over after the sweeping of the glaciers. For a hundred and fifty Shangri-la yards of bank there is limestone underfoot. With a single step – just one stride, mind you – you step off the black acid grind of gneiss onto the tended lawn of a piece of Derbyshire White-Peak, transported to the far bank of a Highland loch. You know you have to change your flies. The steady black team that had worked hard and well down the run of Loch Urigill's southern shore is suddenly all wrong. The water whispers 'ephemera' and there is a seepage of tiny olives, even on this cool wind-fretted day. Take that step through the geological portal, onto the close-crop sweet grass and breathe deeply. But beware. You may never want to step back.

And so here you are again, *Galium sterneri,* at the Keyhole Loch. Not in profusion. But farther on here is Dark-red Helleborine, *Epipactis atrorubens.* Not in flower now – but its tiny red petals are the source of each year's bright red spots on the beautiful fat browns who run twice before lowering their heads to fight.

Come on, Fish Runner. We want a bit of action. Catch us a real fish.

I have knelt to the plants on which this all hangs and now I am ready to cast. Everything is in place. It could come on the first cast. So I am calm from the start. Each cast is the first cast; short and oblique to the bank. At the end of the long traditional lift my flies again become airborne, for just one back-cast, economical, and shoot smoothly; back to their combing of the water. There is no watch or clock in the corrie. It is now and never.

No! This cannot be a fish. The black water itself is humping its back. A charging bull onslaught at my flies and an echo of me starts back at the threat of it. But *I* do not move. There is a tremor in the forearm as a signal to strike arrives simultaneously with the countermand. The nerves roar: 'Wait!' into the silent cathedral of the corrie. This sonnet has not yet turned. Then I lift the rod firmly, questioning. In a quiet, steady voice. Is anybody there? His answer is disproportionate, most out of character: a high launch during which I hear the thrum of his tail slap the face of the air.

Then deep and far and then something is wrong. Twenty

yards of hurry along the shore and I can see it. Such a bright splinter of gold tinsel down in the clear loch. My top dropper, fouled in a crack of the rock while the fish, flanking deeper in the dark, has the point. If I can just reach. There might still be a chance. If I am quick.

You'd think after a run like that he'd be a bit sluggish. But the way he triple-jumped along the bank you'd think he just got out of the car. This could be a really good sequence – plenty of movement. Just so long as he doesn't lose the damned fish.

I know you are calling: fish, plant, rock. I know.

Oh yeah, this is lovely stuff. Look at the pose. You could break to adverts with him frozen just where he is. Up to his waist in water, leaning forwards with one arm reaching down into the deep and the other holding the curved rod high behind him. The arm with the rod looks like a fencer's free arm and his face can only be a few inches off the surface of the water. I bet that's nippy, Fish Runner.

The water is cold and I have always known it is way deeper than it looks. I still resist the idea, even now that it is clear my outstretched right arm, rod held high and back by the left, will not reach nearly far enough. My head bulges sticky and unwilling into the meniscus but finally breaks through. For a moment there is a remote Scottish hill loch with a fly-rod held out from its surface. Before I let go.

Oh fucking hell. Did you see that? Oh fuck, fuck, fuck! Martin, get the Boss. Right now. And you – please leave right now. You never saw a thing. Not a thing. Don't even think about it. We'll be all over you at the first whisper. Martin! I mean *now!*

Fish Runner, you total bastard. Do you know how much money went down to the bottom with you? And me. It took me six months to get a job editing children's shorts for a middle-eastern airline. I thought the Boss was going to pass out right there in the control room. Hell, nothing we could do. Even the helicopter wouldn't have been there for forty minutes. The argocats couldn't get close. The Boss knew what needed doing without having to think about it too much. I got all the archive tapes within the hour and took them down to an old patch of waste ground by the river. Burnt the lot of them. Well, most, eh? Wouldn't do to be too thorough. Of course, there are copies of the programmes themselves. But that's just some footage of a guy fishing. Hard to make any trouble from that.

The funny thing was that the automatic date recording on some of the tapes was duff. I notice things like that. It's my job. I have all the tapes of the day he took a dive – I just thought they might come in useful sometime. Just in case. Most of them aren't of any interest – the first guy on shift would set the cameras running remotely at all the possible locations we thought he might be headed for. The date and time seem to be recording properly on this one tape, but then, late in the day, here comes the Fish Runner – I know, stupid name now he's dead, but I never did get his real name. He's walking, a bit bedraggled, out from Cam Loch. I know it has to be a fault with the date-time recording on the tape because Cam is twenty miles from Keyhole – even as the raven flies.

David Profumo

David Profumo was born in 1955 and taught English before becoming a novelist and freelance writer. His work has appeared in most of the UK's national papers and in many magazines such as *The Spectator, Literary Review, Gray's Sporting Journal, Waterlog, Tatler* and *The Field*. A biographer and award-winning novelist, he was elected a Fellow of the Royal Society of Literature in 1996. His angling volumes include *In Praise of Trout* and the bestselling anthology *The Magic Wheel* of which he was co-editor. His novels include *Sea Music* and *The Weather in Iceland*. David divides his time between Perthshire, London and whichever one of thirty countries he just happens to be fishing in at the time.

The Stepping Stones

In sporting terms, I enjoyed a charmed upbringing. An elderly uncle, who owned a rambling Sutherland estate, adopted me as his apprentice and Augusts were spent learning the twin arts of fly-casting and shooting flying. After cutting my teeth on burn and loch, I was marched onto the lawn with a beer-bottle under my right arm (Mr. Mac, the under-keeper, had thoughtfully drained it for me) and taught to throw a flyline. This was a lodge with a formal Edwardian ethos, and if you intended to win your spurs it had to be according to the traditional rites of passage.

The household was run along similar lines – changing for dinner, charades, a breakfast gong – and if the presiding genius was my uncle (a Tory grandee who'd won an MC with bar in the Great War, and survived a dog-fight with the Red Baron), its tutelary spirit was his butler, Mr. White, a loyal, camp, servant straight from Central Casting. He had two similar chums who took their vacations to coincide with the grouse season, so our picnics on the moor were served by three chaps in uniform, all called George. Factor in that this uncle was a director of Purdeys, and his cartridge bags were fashioned from the skin of a rogue lion he'd been obliged to shoot whilst Governor of West Africa, and you can appreciate that for a schoolboy in the 1970s, this was a heady setting for the summer hols.

I suppose it was his tackle-room that enthralled me most. Here were racks where a dozen or so rods of Palakona and greenheart were horizontally displayed, rigged and ready for action. Numerous cupboards contained the avuncular apparatus of a lifetime spent chasing fish (Victoria was Queen when he was born): winders festooned with lines of dressed silk, battered metal 'otters', a squadron of pre-war Perfects, serried ranks of Hardy Neroda oxblood fly-boxes, cases of Devon minnows no doubt hand-carved by Noah. His great treasure was a mighty hipflask capable of taking three-quarters of a bottle of spirits: nicknamed 'The Admiral', it was a favourite with gillies, though it was not until I turned twenty-one that I was deemed old enough to take my first pull from its silver cup.

My deep yearning to catch a salmon was partly to prove to my family that I could succeed in at least one outdoor activity. I was an unprepossessing adolescent, with lank hair and a face so besmirched by acne that it looked like a pizza with extra pepperoni. At school, I had the misfortune to be bookish at a place that admired athleticism; I could not climb a rope, but I knew lots of useful stuff about Cappadocian foreign policy (decades of scotch have subsequently sluiced such irrelevancies from my brain). Whilst my peers earned their colours on the playing fields where the Battle of Waterloo was won, I freelined cheese paste for chub in a Thames backwater. Somehow, I was not considered officer material.

On the morning of August 15th, 1970, as Mr. White is serving the cold snipe for breakfast, we are informed that the Fleet is in spate, and falling. Outside, the Keeper, Mr. Murray (another George) is fixing rods to the roof of the old Bedford van. He greets me with a conspiratorial, zigzag smile, trademark Silk Cut cupped in his hand: at fourteen, I am going to be allowed to fish the river for the first time.

The Fleet above Rogart is a modest stream with charming meanders, but it runs off quickly after rain, so the window of opportunity is quite small. We are sent to a pool called the Stepping Stones, though with the water still over the banks and the colour of bitter ale there is no sign of the contours that won it that name. I am hefting a borrowed Grant Vibration rod, twelve foot of spliced greenheart with a slow, nodding action that takes a while to master. Luckily, no long casting is required. Ten minutes into the pool, there is a rolling 'rug' at my line, and, at long last, I am on.

A sullen tussle ensues. The salmon planes against the thick current, and I have no experience of how to put the heat on him. There is also the thorny problem of a barbed wire fence submerged between me and the fish. An hour passes, and my Y-fronts are now definitely in a W. The local postie stops off to watch the fun, and my uncle arrives from downstream and inspects his gaff-point. I want to land this prize so much I am praying silently to the Lord Almighty (Fish Division), but still I can not bring it within reach. It shows once, then skulks away. Another forty minutes, and the gaff goes out across the wire – there's nothing wrong with the old aviator's aim – and he's mine: at nine pounds two ounces, a goodish one for that water.

In the evening I am presented with the rod, but somehow I have never dared test its magic again since.

How did I feel? Well, given that my sensations of triumph had until then been pretty limited I felt heroic, like some warrior who had just single-handedly liberated a village. For the first time, I was treated as a grown-up, I had joined the elite, I had graduated from the burns, there was lead in the pencil. Hell, it was better than a lungful of Mexican green.

And there it might have ended, a neat, hermetically sealed experience – except it proved to be just a start, only the first of the stepping stones on a journey that leads from there to here – to this author, years later, hunched over his typewriter, dram in hand, shaking like some laboratory rabbit as he tries to hack out a meagre living as a fishing writer at a desk where a Bogdan acts as paperweight to the unpaid bills in a house on the banks of a Highland loch. I think I've even grown an adipose fin.

Because against all the odds, that uncle and I became fishing buddies for years to come. Whilst still a schoolboy, I fished Shin, Spey, Carron and Brora with my mentor, meeting Rob Wilson, Neil Graesser, and John Ashley-Cooper (only about ten thousand salmon separated us, at that juncture). I was introduced to the great Megan Boyd, who taught me fly-dressing – a bit like popping round to Archimedes for help with the maths prep – and gradually this rare arrangement found its own rhythm. My aunt didn't mind him being away, so long as I was keeping an eye on things, and of course I gained access to some fabulous fishing. Even then, I was aware how deeply privileged I was, with each step we took together.

During my university years, we ventured yet farther afield. In July 1976, we were invited to fish the Upper Restigouche as the guest of K C Irving, proprietor of the Irving oil empire, who had also flown in the Royal Flying Corps. This Canadian experience was the first glimpse I had of real bonanza fishing: the then daily limit was two salmon, both to be killed, and one morning I had to stop before nine a.m. Mind you, a brace weighing 19 and 21 pounds on a dry fly are hardly grounds for complaint. Although into his eighties, my uncle wasn't out of gas yet. This was a man who'd been shot down over Vimy Ridge and neither cataracts nor wobbly hips were going to ground him. Next stop was the Grimersta, where several of his chums from the Lords were members, and it was there that I landed my hundredth Atlantic, and had to buy champagne for the entire lodge.

These were almost incredible opportunities, and we laughed and gossiped our way through it all: he taught me to drink whisky, and appreciate Havanas, and like an osprey I watched him fly-fish, and learned all I could.

Just after I graduated, he gave me perhaps the finest invitation of them all. For some years he had been renting from a ducal pal a prime autumn week on Tweed above Kelso. In those days, the back-end sport was probably approaching its zenith, and as a result of his generosity I fished that beat every October from 1977 until just recently. This is no place for swaggering statistics, but they were bountiful years. At that time, he shared the beat with one other rod, a plutocratic butcher who arrived from the hotel each morning in a Rolls chauffeured by his factotum, Harry, who was famed for his collection of pornography. By now, my Uncle also travelled with Mr. White to lend a helping hand; it was grand to see how the burly boatmen responded to his charm – 'M' Lord,' he'd complain, 'that Fletcher's being cheeky to me again!' It was a colourful group.

One morning I was on my own, fast into a large fish in the stream below the cauld. Mr. White cruised up in his black Sierra. Down went the window: 'Ooh, Mister David, is it a fish?' I replied that it was, and invited him to help me land it. Despite years of service to one of the keenest sportsmen I've ever met, George White had never even held a landing net, let alone the massive one propped up behind the hut. Tottering down the bouldery bank in his striped trousers and Chelsea boots, he peered uncertainly into the margins, as a salmon (that was surely nearer thirty pounds than twenty) came wallowing in towards him. In a moment of typical enthusiasm, he executed a vigorous lunge and, as he raised the net triumphantly, there was just the Waddington, its treble in the meshes, neatly extracted from the scissors of the fish.

Assuring him this was no problem, that another would be along just like a number 19 bus, I went back to the neck of the run. I'm not sure which of us felt worse. But the very next cast – I know this is scarcely credible – there was another take, and this time my new gillie made no mistake. That fish tipped the scales at 21 pounds, but Mr. White never would touch a net again.

My uncle caught his last fish in his ninetieth year, just before he reached that final stone and stepped up onto the other side. Sometimes, as I'm working down a pool he loved, I fancy I see him on that far bank, tamping his pipe or waving companionably to his now middle-aged apprentice. At least he knows the Admiral is in good hands.

Between Honey and Salt

Ever since I hauled my first, mahogany-hued troutling from a lochan high up on the Sutherland moors I have been in thrall to hill waters, and now – almost fifty years later – the landscape my mind automatically conjures up when I hear talk of fishing is not some Rolls-Royce beat on the Spey, nor a pampered stretch of English chalk stream, but rather a place of brawling heather and dark waves that slosh against the shore. Here, you travel light, with a lissom rod and a boxful of straggly flies and a piece packed away in your pocket; covering as much water as time will allow (there's that walk back, remember) you fan out your casts in the knowledge that, however small your glittering prize might prove to be, it will have been stocked by the Almighty.

As any angler will tell you, the allure of such rough, elementary sport has much to do with your unkempt surroundings and their wilderness tang, and it was this quality, so rare to catch in words, that first drew me to the work of the man I personally regard as the bard of Highland hill lovers – the late Norman MacCaig.

Although he spent much of his working life in Edinburgh and Stirling (he was a primary school headmaster, and then a University Reader), MacCaig described himself as 'three quarters Gaelic and one quarter a Borderer'. His mother – a Macleod from Scalpay – had come to the capital as a monoglot Gael, but it was into an Anglophone *ménage* that her son was born, in 1910. The young Norman first visited his Hebridean relations at the age of twelve, and both the topography and the culture of the islands made an impression on his subsequent verse, helping to shape his 'strong preference for poetry with hard outlines.' But the most pronounced influence on his visual imagination was to be the landscape of North-West Sutherland, which he discovered just before the Second World War (being a pacifist, he went to prison for his beliefs) and where for many years he had a croft at Achmelvich, by

Inverkirkaig, dwelling, as he phrased, it between 'Honey and salt – land smell and sea smell'. With the possible exception of George Mackay Brown, I can think of no other modern poet writing in English who has so accessibly evoked the wilder aspects of Scotland; indeed, the region adopted by the self-styled 'man in Assynt' as his spiritual home is now thought of by his admirers as 'MacCaig country'.

Drive north from Ullapool to Kylesku and all that lies to your left was the inspiration to this remarkable man for some fifty years – in effect, the catchment area of those two little rivers the Kirkaig and the Polly. The geology here in the Caledonian outback is ancient and complex, involving bosses of Archaean gneiss – some of the world's oldest rock – with isolated Torridonian peaks: Cul Beag, Cul Mor and Stac Pollaidh (*anglice* Stack Polly, favourite of climbers) to the south, then Canisp and Quinag (the 'water stoup') and at its heart the colossal pillar of Suilven with its pink sandstone terraces and its arrowhead summit making a stab at the heavens. Sentimental visitors dub this 'God's own country', but as an atheist of some commitment Norman MacCaig would have balked at that. Still, it is not difficult to divine whence came that liking for 'hard outlines' in his poetry, nor to guess at the source of its clear, mineral strength.

By all accounts he was a vigorous walker of these hinter-lands, and his verses are full of rockscape and water. In poem after poem he takes to the mountains ('The tall cliffs unstun my mind'), and naturally Suilven itself afforded him numerous lofty vistas – 'the little loch/ is the one clear pane/ in a stained-glass window' – and opportunities to tinker with perspective, a particular fondness of his. He once insisted that nearly all his poems were about things that had actually happened, which may account for the rare immediacy about his descriptions of raven and Bell heather, waterfall and deer. 'Landscape and I get on well together,' he wrote, but that scarcely explains how his vocabulary and metaphor work so closely with the grain of their subject.

He also enjoyed his fishing. Whether dapping for sea trout

or hoiking out mackerel, it's a pastime that features in dozens of his poems, and he expressed his preference unequivocally: 'There's something to be obsessed with for all of us. /Mine is lochs, the smaller the better.' The terrain around Suilven – being largely the same gneiss as the Western Isles – is blessed with a mass of these smaller waters, some (like Borralan) holding char, others ferox (Loch Fionn) but mostly just modest native brownies, maybe three to the pound. Such hill lochs vary dramatically in character. One may be entrancingly frosted with water lilies, yet yields mere fingerlings; whereas its neighbour, beetle-browed and dour of aspect beneath its crags, might bestow on you an astonishing pounder. It is this diversity that intrigues the poet, rather than any heroic piscatorial potential: his closing image to 'Loch Sionascaig' is typically modest, the leaping trout ('Heraldic figure on a shield of spray') being followed by the only mark the poet reckons he leaves, his footprint disappearing in the 'the puddled sand'.

Why is it that so many poets have been fishers? Lang, Hogg, Buchan, Yeats, Lowell, the last two Poets Laureate – is it something to do with having to keep a weather eye open, or the need to speculate, or even the desire for formal perfection? Surely a reflective quality links the two casts of mind, and there might conceivably be a rhythmic connection there (*homo piscatorius* is generally attuned to the sharps and flats of running water)… Well, let's not worry about that now, because our trudge up this corrie has at last brought us to the Loch of the Rowans – the wind seems to be about right, so let's make our first cast here from the promontory, where that dove-grey rock bursts through the peat. I've a Zulu on the bob, followed by the Soldier Palmer, and a classic Grouse and Claret on the point. They flirt deliciously along the ripple, this evening's light making the water look like strong whisky. Nothing that time, though it's good just to be working the line out to my satisfaction, after a week wasted in the city. There – a small convulsion below the surface, but he missed it. Again – this time I set the iron and he's on, lugging away at once toward the refuge of the reeds; but I want him for dinner, and his skirmish proves futile. Before long he lies shivering on the boulder, all ten ounces of him, flanks gleaming like a spoon through treacle.

All sportsmen have memories of companions from their formative years and I find as I grow older that I fish with them in mind, especially in certain spots. This human factor – the association of people with particular places – often intensifies the further away you go from the world of artificial human concerns. There is an element of this throughout MacCaig's work, not only in the Scalpay poems, but in his finest volume (*The Equal Skies*, 1980) with its dozen brief elegies for his great sporting friend Angus MacLeod, who is seen as having become the *genius loci* of the poet's adoptive world – 'the landscape I love best/ and the man who was its meaning and added to it…' So in the end MacCaig is sustained by his memory of these places they have explored together, dragging boats for miles and fishing for salmon and drinking into the night. It helps to explain how the poet himself in later years has 'returned/ to suck the honey of Assynt/ and want no more.'

And indeed what more could one want from any part of the world than the sweetness of a true homecoming?

The Wilderness Cure

My father-in-law has a little hideaway on Harris in the Western Isles of Scotland. This great outcrop of Archaean gneiss – at 3,000 million years old, one of Europe's more ancient bits – Harris is a rocky skeleton in a blanket of kelp, an intractable land of peathags and hillocks where sheep browse, seabirds squall, and the ozone hits you like a cocktail. In British terms, this is a very remote community: even mainland Scots are regarded as foreigners, and the likes of us from the South – though treated with great politeness – are known as 'white settlers'. Yet I often think there must be something of witch-beauty in these harsh, broken places: for what else could account for the glamorous spell they seem to cast over certain visitors?

You get to the house by a two-mile hike from the nearest road, alongside a loch which, for convenience rather than any proprietorial motives, is called the House Loch. Our Hebridean sojourns depend on it, however: it supplies our water directly through a hosepipe down the brae (no fancy UV filtration here), the peaty traces making a grand brew of morning tea, and also releasing the nose of your evening malt. When first I stumbled along this path, it was dark, a storm was yowling across the moor, and the only torch was in the possession of The Doctor (as my now father-in-law is known); from the crashing of water on rocks down to my right I assumed we were teetering along a perilous sea cliff, as my guide strode off ahead. At that moment neither of us would have guessed how that loch was to become an abiding feature of my future. I was just his daughter's latest boyfriend, and The Doctor was testing my mettle: a few summers later, I got engaged on its very banks.

Though perhaps not much more than ten acres in extent, the loch has many of the classic contours of bigger waters, plus the added appeal of an intimate scale – with its cliffs, narrows, skerries and promontories it could be a bonsai Lomond or Maree. Lying right by the sea, it picks up contrary winds and

140

even the mountain ash that sprouts from crevices of relative shelter is stunted and salt-burned. Invisible from any house or road, the loch is scarcely ever fished. I've been just feet away from otters here around dusk, and once a huge sea eagle wheeled overhead. A couple of hours will suffice to cast round its heavily indented shoreline, and then, if the fish all seem to have gone away to some trout convention elsewhere, you can just sprawl on the heather and watch the rocks grow.

Short of pirking for pollack off Rockall, this is about as wild as fishing in Britain can get. For thirty-three summers now this has been the place where I go to get my Wilderness Cure.

I am possessed by the desire to fish, but much of my year is spent in the metropolis. There's only so much fun you can have flicking peanuts to the koi carp that cruise in our local park fountain. If I want an awayday with the fly rod it tends to result in stew-bred stockies lumbering around some Home Counties pond (at one of which, recently, the proprietor turned on some floodlights towards the end of the day 'to prolong the sport'). Now, I've nothing against hatchery fish *per se* – without them, people like me would have far fewer angling opportunities – but whenever possible I like to get back to the natural challenge of these farflung waters which, however modest many of their denizens might be, are stocked by the Creator. And if the day ever comes when I find I'm tired of trying for these small, trim, dark-enamelled loch brownies and am pining for the fudge coloured Porky Pigs of the southern put-and-take waters, then I'll know it's time to swap my rod for a niblick.

The Hebridan lochs vary dramatically between the most fertile shellsand (or *machair*) waters of Uist, that can produce big, butter-fat brown trout, and the more peaty, acidic, moorland lochs of Lewis and Harris. The latter are often oligotrophic – containing little in the way of dissolved salts that would promote plant life, and the invertebrate food web – but only experience will tell which systems are the exception. In the

House Loch, for instance, I have found evidence – in the pabulum taken from trout stomachs – of sticklebacks and water beetle (corixa), which probably explains why surface-rising fish are rare; yet not a hundred yards away is another loch, with its own little feeder burn, that seems to yield trout no larger than gudgeon.

Although they seem few and far between, the trout you do get on 'our' loch can be lovely fish – 'as plump as little aldermen, and a great deal livelier', in Arthur Ransome's nice phrase. Most are smaller than herrings, and each year I take a few – if I can – and we eat them within the hour, with oatmeal and bacon, savouring this simple harvest as fish epicurism at its finest. For the most part they are returned, flanks gleaming; such trout are living national treasures, direct descendants of fish landlocked thousands of years ago. I believe that in these parts the population of each separate loch is slightly distinct, and that where our hunger does not dictate killing, we should be content to borrow. Ethics are theoretical much of the time anyway, since the fish are damnably hard to catch.

Indeed, the House Loch is almost preternaturally unpredictable: even after three decades of studying its summer moods I am still unable to second-guess my chances, and many's the time I have felt it all looked ideal (a westerly zephyr, cloud ceiling high and broken) and I might as well have been flogging the corrugated tin roof of The Doctor's outhouse. I relish this sort of challenge, but the major drawback has been that it does not make for an ideal beginner's water. The attention span of children seems to be about ten minutes, if fish are not 'biting'; if you can't show them a good time, impromptu peat-lobbing competitions will ensue and then your prospects sink to zero. If the midges of Harris are biting you can forget any initiation into the 'gentle art of angling' altogether. Therefore when it came to the crucial matter of trying to arrange for my sons to become connected to their first fish – and *enjoy the experience* – I took a garden fork and a jam-jar with a perforated lid to the potato patch, and bent to my paternal task.

There is much to be said for the worm, and personally, I don't give a Donald Duck about purism at all costs – though The Doctor, I must say, winces whenever I produce my spinning rod. James, Tom and I floatfished merrily for several summers, and then they seemed quite keen to try my own preferred method, at which point I knew they themselves were hooked. To me, much of the pleasure of this sort of fishing lies in the use of light tackle: a three-weight fly rod, a waistcoat with the minimum of clobber in the pockets, and you just slip out of the door once all chores are done, slog up the hill, and you should be casting within five minutes. I keep tactics pretty simple: a tiny goldhead nymph in the calm, a Pennell if there's a decent ripple, and an Invicta in the gloaming: we're up there on the rocks to have fun, not make piscatorial history.

A burn runs out of the loch and down beside the house. Each year, we construct an elaborate dam with tussocks and turf, and thus create a holding pool to which the odd captive is transferred. With a good spate, sticklebacks washed down from the loch above will materialize there overnight like shoals of miniature tuna. In low water, I take my underwater Aquascope up through the shrunken pools and we guddle out bootlace eels and troutlings from their hidey-holes. But the fish are definitely fewer since the escapee mink moved in. They have devoured the rabbits and the rats and the birds, and many of the trout. Last year, when the boys and I were doing a spot of target practice with an air pistol by the house, a mink popped up in our little dam pool and stared insolently at me, not fifteen feet away in broad daylight. You could wait all your life for a shot like that (I missed clean, naturally).

I never knew there were sizeable trout around until a few years ago when a two-day storm suddenly exhausted itself just before dark and something prompted me to forsake the smoky comforts of the peat hearth and try the near arm of the loch. In that curious yellow and grey glare you get after a big wind I flung a hairy great Soldier Palmer out into the wave, and at first I reckoned I had snagged Scotland. When I slid him ashore, that trout weighed over two pounds – about eight times larger than the average. The other I took was on a blazing August afternoon, when I'd just sauntered up for some casting practice: this one grabbed my fly as if it belonged to him, and after a tense struggle on fine nylon I went down the rockface to hoik him out. He weighed in at 1lb 12oz, and my wife knew there was something up when I stuck my head round the door, grinning like a Pathan tribesman who had just been given a hard-boiled egg.

One evening, as I was returning – rodless – from the road, I saw a much bigger fish, certainly the size of a summer salmon, move twice by a weed bed. At least, I suppose it was a fish.

There used to be dozens of families dwelling on this headland, but today only our friend Rachel remains. Now in her eighties, she is the last of the traditional Gaelic storytellers. Recently, taking tea with her, I enquired whether the loch had a real name.

'Well,' she began, with that soft intake of breath so characteristic of the Hebrideans, 'we used to know it as *lochan caorunn* – the little loch of the rowan.' I sensed she was deliberating whether or not to confide in a 'white settler'. When she continued, Rachel was not repeating fireside gossip, but something darker. 'Within my father's memory there were five brothers living around the loch here, and one evening, after feeding his family a meal of shellfish, one saw from his door a water-horse come up out of the loch and start to rummage around, you know, in the empty shells. And so the man went in, and he said: 'That's it for us in this place.' And that whole family from out here, they left on the next boat to Manitoba.'

The water-horse, kelpie or *each-uisge* was not a joke: this demon dragged girls underwater, and devoured all but the lungs. Almost every loch in the Highlands and Islands harbours such a myth, if you enquire.

These days I take no risks, and fish barbless.

Dexter Petley

Dexter Petley is a novelist, translator, editor and angling writer. His four critically acclaimed novels are *Little Nineveh, Joyride, White Lies* and *One True Void*. His translations include *The Fishing Box* by Maurice Genevoix. Dexter lives in a caravan in Normandy, surviving on organic permaculture, mushroom hunting, rainwater, foraging winter fuel and old birds' nests to decorate the wattle sides of his dry toilet. He is the 'dp' half of *Letters from Arcadia* on the *Caught by the River* website http://caughtbytheriver.net. His longer angling writing has appeared in *Waterlog* magazine.

Carp-horse Bob

A south-easterly in June coshes the Low Maynard into froth. Brown water swills over the steps up the dam end as the rain skins your face. Just the three of you, a quarter-mile apart on twenty-nine acres of London tapwater, the Walthamstow Reservoirs, ten barren concrete bowls built by the old Metropolitan Water Board in the reign of King George and Queen Mary.

You're out in Zone 3 on the Victoria Line, the cutting edge of Tottenham marshes between the Coppermill Stream and the old River Lea. Midweek. Treeless scrub, wind grating through pylons. The spit and smell of a toothpaste factory. You can see the floodlights of White Hart Lane turn to bilge. Arctic terns screel overhead as you chuck a drenched sandwich at the Brent geese. You can see red buses going by the gates half a mile away, tyres slishing in the wet, headlights on gloss.

By now the rain has soaked in. It drips from your neck down to the insides of your socks. You just can't be bothered to pack up and walk back to the tube station. Your wax jacket is stiff as card and you feel like Ned Kelly. Your army rucksack is a sponge, your landing net has put on 10lbs of sky. On a crowded tube you're going to stink of last season's carp slime. You'll drip gallons of regurgitated rain on the train floor. You're like a papier mâché monster, a stink-bomb you just add water to, soggier than any tramp. All the perfumed commuters will edge away as the dripping turns to a pool lapping round the soft Italian shoes and the Fenwick's carrier bags. If anyone touches you it's a ten-quid dry cleaner's bill. You will look even worse if you carry the dead weight of another blank on the Maynard again, like you did nine times out of ten in those days, the mid-1980s.

What keeps you going day after day is the false danger. On late-night tube trains wearing combat gear on summer nights. The image of being an élite hunter of monster carp in the middle of London, like Bladerunner for the Carp Society. The suddenness of being out there in bleakest, solitary Tottenham wasteland. It was here, in the 1970s, that Thames Water carried out an experiment in water maintenance. They stocked the reservoirs with 20,000 carp, fast-growing triploid stockies, an Italian mirror strain which packed on over 3lbs a year. By 1980 fishing in London was avant-garde. A handful of pioneers stalking round these concrete bowls in an everlasting wind.

And now in the cold June rain you have no choice. You wait for the rush-hour to pass. You hope the rain will stop by evening and you can dry your 42-inch landing net in the wind. With no sun you can't tell the time. The angler three hundred yards away on the opposite bank is invisible, crouching between a gap in the brambles. The third bloke looks like he's moving up your way. None of us has packed an umbrella. It was like that on the Maynard. Storms blew in off the estuary, across the marshes. You could spend all day snapping guy ropes and bending skewers if your umbrella didn't just implode and take your eye out before launching itself onto the waves and sinking in thirty feet of water.

The '80s Maynard is a heartbreak place. Anglers go all season there without a bite. Your best chance is mobility, reconnaissance, binoculars. A fish crashes a hundred yards away and you should have a bait on its nose within five minutes. An extra 30lbs of metal umbrella protracts your response, and you're going to get wet anyway. Just try dragging all that gear up and down broken escalators, squeezing down the aisle of a double-decker bus or a pin-stripe carriage. At least they let you on a bloody train. Bus conductors take one look and say: *oh no mate, you ain ge'n on my bus like that.* So, you stay mobile, travel light, unless it rains.

The gates are locked half an hour after sunset. At the end of June you're climbing over the spiked railings at 10.45 p.m. Last knockings, the only chance of a fish if there's a sun. Low Maynard fish knew that. They mocked you as you packed in against the clock. Rolling the water to a pulp exactly where your baits were the minute you reeled them in. You can always duck it out and poach till eleven. The last tube goes through to Victoria at midnight. If you hook a fish after eleven it's a big deal, a long fight in the dark, a big fuss as you staunch your flashlight, lose your rod-rest. You get slime on the sleeves you've just rolled down against the gathering chill, slime on your weighing net and camera after you've guessed where the fish is for the flash photos you hope won't attract a bailiff. And night fish always tail-whack when you put them back and give your neck a complete last drenching. On top of this you already have a dreaded sweat. It really is a long jog to the tube station, up past the warehouses and the gypo camp behind the hoardings. Catch, and you are weightless with triumph. Blank, and you drag the lead of failure, struggle, ache, and stink.

On a calm warm night a bailiff will drive round in the Land Rover and sweep his searchlight along the margins after the poachers. You have to hide the gear then, lay flat in the brambles, loosen the clutch right down so the fish can run if it dares take a bait now. Somehow you have to stuff that rod flat in the water, wedge it so the carp can't drag it in. But in weather like today no one will come. It's a piss-out. You'll be on your own after lock-in. And you're thinking this because you can't move, the rain has rendered you incapable of decision. Or is it because the carp have begun to dance?

They move on the wind in one great pulse. Like rolling dolphins north at sea, launching over waves, a hundred yards and closing, fifty yards, then one smacks the water in front of you. Red-eyed, orange belly, it stares for one second, then disappears in a fist of bubbles, the flat spot of its presence is only wiped clean by the waves when they break against the shore.

The angler on the opposite bank stands up between his bramble thickets. The third bloke is walking down, following the fish. You know this hard, bleak water well. You know the hope is false. The carp binge on daphnia and zooplankton suspended in the upper layer. Bait is of little interest. They can stay like this for days and you wouldn't get a tremble on your line. More depressing than your certainty of failure is the hope your two companions seem to have. The angler opposite is baiting up. The gulls pick off his baits as he catapults them seventy yards on a crosswind. The tufted ducks sub down and come up ten seconds later with his little red balls in their beaks. The gulls bomb the tufties. The tufties dive again to keep the bait. The angler tries to divert them by catapulting stones the other way. Something we all go through. Nowadays, you just have to get your catapult out of the rucksack and the Arctic terns are on to you, like Stukas and snipers.

On the wind you hear a voice. Strangled rage, throttled bitterness. The only distinguishable words're 'fark' and 'borstard'. This is how a carp swears underwater. But it's not a carp shouting in the wind, or even a half carp. It's Aardvark. You wished you'd packed up.

Aardvark bears the insults of the world. Stone, rock, mountain-deaf. He lip-reads, but there's always someone else's hook in the lip, never his own. He's not incapable of catching carp, but just before he might, it all goes wrong. His silent world is too easily invaded by his own voice. His words are angry hornets coming and going all day. You hear him coming down with the carp. You call him Aardvark because it's like he says Aarrrr-varrrk every fuckin minute he's alive.

— Farrrrckin barrrrstard, he shouts now. Ah said e'd farkin do thart. Aardvark, twenny parnd! Up his arse twenny parnd.

You've stayed under the only trees in a thousand acres. Aardvark dumps his gear in the mud behind the next swim, twenty feet away. Squeezing in, he thinks you're on the fish. You wonder if he's even seen you. He's shouting: Aaawww bloody hell. The elastic on his catapult tangles round his rucksack buckle. He's wearing his Australian bush hat with the fish hooks in. Drooping and soggy. His wide tree-trunk jeans flap like wet sails on a dingy. He keeps up his moan, like the wind in his wires, like he's forgotten that silence is a natural condition and that pretending not to be deaf does not involve making a noise. Does he even know he's audible?

You stand behind him but he's in a world of his own. His tackle is like a fallen pylon, a congealed parody of recognisable parts. Tangled metal, swinging leads, twisted lines.

Nothing serves him. All is opposition. Diversion. Camouflage. And it's like Aardvark lives in a sinking world which he bails out ad infinitum just to keep afloat.

He snatches two bulging carrier bags off himself and plunges a fat hand into one. The other spills. His free hand yanks at the catapult. It thwocks free, sending shards of its last soggings into his face. He paws fistfuls of red, reeking black-eyed beans into it. They scatter over his boots, down his arm, into the mud he's begun to make with his tractor feet. He aims into the wind and fires like in terror at a stampede. A quick pickling of beans pocks the water, the rest come down in a shower over you, Aardvark, and the mud. Like a near-miss from a trench mortar. This time he plunges into the other bag and dredges out a sod of chic peas dyed orange and reeking of Scopex. You take cover as the pug comes down. The more demented he becomes, the fewer pultfuls hit the water. You start to shout uselessly. He won't look. You can't get near him for divits of bait and tackle-block. He blames the cata-pult now in a stream of incoherence. He tries to snap it like a wishbone. He stretches it. Two feet, three feet, another inch and fack! The clips give and it smacks him like he wanted it to. He hurls it right into your swim and it hangs like a busted bra on your line.

This time you really shout. He's got hearing aids on each ear, big plastic boxes like electronic bite alarms, the really crap ones you get in tackle shops which really sell pet food and Chinese screwdrivers. When they get drenched they sound like Stockhausan. Is that Aardvark's trouble? Atonal tinitus in his bite alarms? Does he have to lay down between his rods and hook the line round the back of his ears? He never seemed to trust his eyes, always leaping up and down thinking he'd got a take, that a carp was pulling at his ear-ache.

He starts shovelling the black-eyes in with his hands. This isn't baiting the swim. This is a man attacking imaginary foes. And in your daze you're too slow to step aside as he swings round and clambers up the bank. His square face battered in pain and Red Zing like running mascara, tears of blood which

151

he spits and mingles with snot pendulums.

— THAT'S MY SWIM, you shout.

He slips as he tries to come forward. His hands make perfect prints in the mud. You wonder if some geologist 600,000 million years from now will...

— YEOW DON OWN THE FARKIN LAKE YER FARKIN BORSTARD, he shouts.

You step back, and back. The force of his voice is like the kick-back on a shotgun. He doesn't compensate for it and his blasting away only hampers his lunging forward until he trips over his rods.

— AH'M JARSS FED UP, FED UP WITH THE LART OF YOW. AH KNOW YOUR FARKIN SORT, FARKIN KNOW-IT-ALLS...

You get behind the tree. The rain is colder and seems to go up your trousers as well as down them now. The cloy of Scopex staunches the toothpaste factory. You can see it's gone 8 o'clock. The visible buildings have lights on. There's a roar from White Hart Lane. You can hear the train all stations to St Albans announced on the tannoy at Tottenham Hale.

You can tell the angler opposite is watching your performance. A clump and ploughing of gear makes you turn round. Aardvark's there. The first sack of peas wheels against the unpruned runners on the tree trunk, looping and splitting. Without force it slumps and spills. The second chops you in the collar. Instinctively you clutch at it, let go, get away from it. A burst of Scopex. You smell like a sweet factory. It feels like wet-rot. You slip on a black-eyed bean carpet.

— YOW BORSTARD, Aardvark shouts. His lips hardly move. He'd make a good ventriloquist. You want to see if the other bloke's watching. And again, as if you aren't there, Aardvark slaps away through puddles, all his gear splayed the way it fell as he scoops it into his arms, 2oz leads swinging his rods out of kilter, Aardvark swinging them back, the whole rig jumping free and snagging in the bushes. Everything lands in a clatter again. Garden chair, rucksack, rod rests, landing net pole. He yanks at the rods. Both rigs are seriously snagged. He swishes till you think the rods'll explode into carbon splinters. He wants this to happen but it doesn't, so he walks backwards and you're suddenly in projectile range of two torpedo shaped leads if they come out of that bush. On 15lb line they'll come out at 100mph. You know this for fact. You've seen crack-offs from wannabe tournament casters, suicidal power wind-ups high off the opposite bank. They whack it your way and a kink in the line catches on the launch. A crack-off, the lead flies three hundred yards and embeds itself into the tree beside you. So you run as Aardvark walks further and further backwards, cursing as his line stretches, double its length, cursing you all the time.

— YOW BORSTARD, AH'LL GET MY MATES ON YOU, AH FARKIN GET MY MATES AN CARM BACK AN SORT YOW ART, TAKE THE FARKIN GRIN OFF YOW FACE...

You can only hear him now. Two hundred yards off you can still make out his 'fark' and 'borstard'. You walk back along the trees and there he is, sitting down on his garden chair with the orange flowers. You can't believe he still intends to fish. One of his rod-rests is in the ground but he's bent it on the stones. He's up again, rifling in his pile of gear. No bait.

— AW FARK E'S GOT MY FARKIN BAIT NOW. I'LL SORT 'IS LOT ART...

And then you hear them coming. The beating hooves. Aardvark doesn't even feel them. Unless he feels everything, and hears everything, and none of it's distinguishable from insult. Or is it the rain drumming on his hat? Does he think you're throwing the rain at him? Is that why he threw his particles at you? But the drumming quickens. Is it your heart?

You flip your hood back. And there they are, really, cantering along the trees. Aardvark is sitting on his chair in the middle of the track. You start to run forward and the horses see you first. You can't save him anyway. The horses have a piebald leader and they jostle behind him as he prepares to jump over Aardvark. At first you content yourself; they belong to the gypsies behind the hoarding so you expect to see a drover, hear a command. But the stallion's jumped. He comes down the other side of Aardvark, cleared him by a yard. The others jump the gear or tear up the high bank, along the fringe of the Lockwood reservoir, only to come down behind you. Aardvark's still sitting there. You can't tell if he's seen the horses. Or if they've stilled him, or come from his mind. He could be dead. Or are they his final proof of the world's malignance? His apocalypse? His fuckin mates come to sort you out? So, his asphyxiated language is 'horse' or like a dog-whistle. It whispers to horses, his familiars.

You're actually afraid. They've singled you out. The big piebald stallion snorts at the fore. This is no random escape. The others descend in size to a black foal who throws his head in a frenzy at the wind. The stallion comes forward to smell you. Where's the bait? he says. He noses through your jacket pockets. You've backed into your swim now. You can smell what they can smell. Appetite stimulator, Equivite, 250mls of 1000-to-1 Scopex, Red Zing and Amino Acid and Essential Oil of Horse Pasture and Sugar Lump Extract and Carrot Gold and Gee-up Smack and Walk-On Crack. Yeah, pure Carp Horse.

You start to dump Aardvaak's beans in handfuls. The stallion nudges you aside. He doesn't eat them. He spits them out. It's the Carp Horse they're after. And it's just air, and scent. It's all over you. It's in your rucksack, your hair, in the mud, on the tree. One of the horses swims out to the middle. A carp rolls beside it. The foal's got your rucksack in its teeth. It runs up the bank of the Lockwood and disappears over the lip. You run after it, sliding down again until you take it slowly on your hands and feet like a horse. Once up there you can see the lights of Tottenham coming on, smell the toothpaste factory again. A train to Cambridge pulls away from Tottenham Hale. You're level with the tree tops. The foal's galloping along the concrete lip a hundred yards away. You look down on your swim. A scraggy pit pony with bald legs is sitting on your Lafuma low-chair.

Bob Down Valium Valley

Down Tottenham Hale tube station, that night in 1986, on an empty platform, we both had carp rods, Barbours, rucksacks, both waiting for the last train to Victoria, two human sponges trying to light wet fags from drowned pockets. We stare at each other in disbelief, both thinking the same thing: Christ, is that what I look like when I get on the fucking train?

— Was that you, he says, with those horses?

Bob had been that angler on the other side. In the long ride between stations we shouted about carp fishing over the deafening clatter of the carriages. Some friendships start like a screaming take in the margins. Even shouting, Bob's wisdom had a calmness it was a privilege to listen to after Aardvaak's clamour.

Up Walthamstow Reservoirs they called Bob 'Catweazle'. Some readers might remember Catweazle from kids' TV in the seventies: the Medieval wizard who materialises in the twentieth century after falling in a carp pond. Apart from an obvious resemblance, there *is* something anachronistic about Bob. He knows his place in time and has stuck to it. Even today the rods are contemporary, his knowledge is 'stop press', but he retains that spirit of carp fishing formed in the pivot between the sixties and seventies. He looked like Richard Brautigan; long grey hair with tint of nicotine, like frayed rope washed up on the beach, a billy goat's ruff, that leather jacket from Oxfam with the safari belt, double-breasted, lapels like elephant ears, the smell of indoors, really indoors. Think of that foxed cover of *Trout Fishing in America*. He could have been the original. These days he's modernized the look, backwoods-metro, bait-company caps and tackle-shop Gortex. Gear on the mountain bike, the world seen through Optix, but he's still a Blues man with a lick in his fingers and a song a day.

For the twenty-two years I've known him, Bob's remained one of those constancies in a commodified pastime, an upholder of authentic values in an angling world as fragmented as a shattered window. He fishes with a slow application of wisdom he's collected like a raft of debris in a backwater, like he's painting a fence on a hot summer afternoon, a slowness which includes organisational difficulties, a certain dithering, a pause for philosophical interlude. His coherence in the midst of chaos is exceptional. His gaze is a long one, he fishes like he has all the time in the world, even if his daily life decisions are as last minute as his angling knowledge. If he really was painting a fence and it pissed down, he'd paint on, but with the expressed pessimism of having it ruined.

Bob's a survivor, a survivor of each decade and their dangers. An addict since he went to India in 1971 in a yellow 2CV to join a rock band called The Alley Cats who smashed up their guitars and got knifed in Baghdad alleyways. There's even a danger in writing non-fiction on Bob. I have to de-fictionalize him, and it's kind of a booby trap. Elsewhere, I reinvented him, but in his own colours, from the stories he told me on the banks of The Low Maynard where I found him most afternoons in the summer of '86.

At the time he lived in a crummy bedsit in Stockwell with a cat who never saw daylight and all four walls covered from floor to ceiling with stacks of vinyl, sci-fi paperbacks and every angling magazine there ever was. You sat for five minutes on his black leather chairs scaled with hide-fatigue and you went home smelling like an ashtray in a boilie dip. You had to undress the minute you got in the door and wash the nicotine swamp and Scopex deodorant from every soured stitch. Lend him a book and it never smelt of you again. It reminded you of every tackle shop and bus depot in the world. His glaucal kitchen was a laboratory of bait flavours and additives, his bedsit a memory of every fag he'd ever smoked. The windows never opened and he never tried them to see if they could.

I've known several kindred dwellers, kin to Bob that is. Somehow London institutionalises them, but it's the damage of their past, the insomnia which wrecks their melanin production. Bob once told me he didn't sleep for twenty-nine days, the only time he did cold turkey. But unlike those other Londoners, Bob has a double life in the outside world.

He was usually late up the Maynard, never in a hurry to fish, content to scan the banks with his legs. The difference between Bob and the other London insomniacs is his desire to haunt the waterside, his readiness to trap that insomnia with his rods like it was a fish. I don't think it was so much the miracle of being alive; you had to wonder how he'd lived so long. His daily intake, the fuel for that particular and monstrous engine, was twenty fags, five bars of chocolate, a dozen teas with five sugars each, and a mass pre-bait in milligrams of Valium and Methadone. He was always broke. The system was against him. The black-eyed dog was always looking for his door. The cat is long gone.

But so Compleat an Angler I have never known, albeit a one-species angler, a one-foot-over-the-edge angler whose will to fish is the pump in his heart. His kind heart too, for the man has a generosity akin to nature, a second nature, a sagacity even recognised and applied to by his mental or hierarchical opposites, South London lads half his age who benefit from Bob's calm maturity which is nowhere else to be found.

But let's not get sentimental here. Bob attracts the stuff of stories along with the carp. I don't remember where it was exactly, some gravel pit backing onto the Thames, West of London. The first outing we made away together from Walthamstow. In those days Bob was a Clapham Common bum, one of a faithful posse of Giro men who lived round that ornamental concrete bowl, keeping the burger van alive and practising the nearest thing in carp angling to occupational therapy I've ever seen. The carp too needed psychiatric care; an autistic shoal perilously poised between precocity and hunger, which meant that a hooking was a suicide, a deliberate decision to eat and be damned. The only natural food in the green water were bits of bacon sandwich tossed from the burger van. It was there that Bob met so-and-so or know-who-I-mean, and sometimes one of them had a car and knew some pit in Middlesex where you get ten runs a night. Someone like Austen.

Austen was a proto-lemming. He may've been twenty-one. He sparked on a short fuse and longed to burn out in the stock exchange or a BMW crash. For the moment he was a lowly clerk with fancy carp rods he didn't so much want to see bend on his own, he just demanded a ring of bright public to applaud him. So he chose the Clapham arena, apprentice ponds for many better known anglers, but his patience and skills fell short, his boasting about what he just caught yesterday, elsewhere, matched the secrecy about these waters, the curious reluctance to even take a photograph of those fish in case anyone should guess where they were caught and spoil it for him. Everything was rightfully his, but destined to be out of reach. Bob's constancy must've irked Austen. He needed to impress and possess, so he finally stumped up a weekend fishing on his favourite waters out of town, some club where he could take a guest. He just wanted to show Bob he was the carp-man out there, but Bob badgered him into taking me along too. Austen, being a coot, said alright, but we had to make our own way over to his parents' house first. Just because he had a car didn't mean he had time to come and pick us up.

Austen was class-ridden to the point of anxiety. His parents might've been chemists, something like that, elevated shopkeepers. Me and Bob weren't even supposed to ring his doorbell in case the elevated shopkeepers saw us and died of shame. We waited discreetly near the car, but not at it, again in case suspicions were aroused by the class police. Austen's representation of his life must've been fictitious on all fronts. It was evening, a Friday night. Me and Bob were sweating from the long haul from the bus stop with our rods, pots and pans, bed-chairs and sleeping bags. We were fishing till Sunday afternoon. Early September and the evening about to fall rapidly, but Austen didn't want us to know where we were going. He wanted us to go blindfold and arrive after dark.

He finally came out with ten porters worth of gear. The car was an Austin Allegro. He looked at me and said:

— He can't fuckin come, Bob. There's no room.

We'd never met before, the introduction still delayed.

— Calm down Austen, Bob said. You don't need all that gear. By the way, this is Dexter.

— That's only the first lot. Christ, Bob, you don't know where we're going. Shit, I need my tub of maples.

He fetched a big white plastic dustbin with a lid on, dragging it across the road, prising off the lid in a creak like the stone rolling back from Jesus's tomb.

— Look at them, he said. Take a whiff.

Didn't need to. Smelt like Jesus too. Blew our wigs off.

— Ah Christ, Austen, Bob said. I'm not sitting in the car with that lot. You only need a bag full.

— Not where we're going, Bob. You have to mass bait, really fill it in. I've had these maples on the go for two months now.

We arrived in total darkness, and this was by entrapment. Suddenly this wasn't our real destination, just a hard pit which Austen had mastered, only if he didn't re-master it again we'd be going elsewhere. He insisted we leave our own gear by the car and help carry his.

— I get first choice, he said. You're my guests. I drove you here…

Then he ordered us to watch him get his rods out and rig up, everything tumbling out of sight in the dark.

— Make us a cup of tea while you've nothing better to do then Bob.

The idea was for Austen to cast a hundred yards into the night and get a run in ten minutes.

— Bet I get a take first cast. You wait, I've done it loads of times. I've really got 'em going on my baits.

Me and Bob hadn't eaten. It was 10 p.m. While we'd been waiting in Austen's street, he'd been having supper. Said he got in late because he'd been to his mobile phone class or the health club, I can't remember. Anyway, he had his cast. Not far enough.

— Wait, watch this. I can cast further… See, that was a hundred yards. I'll get a run now… No, wait, what's fucking wrong with you two. Set up in the next swim if you're in such a hurry.

Me and Bob went back for our gear, our hearts just not in the fishing. Because we'd had to carry everything by foot, we hadn't lugged much grub along, making Austen promise to stop at a shop, a promise easily broken. On the way he'd pulled into a service station to fill up with petrol and got back into the car stuffing chocolate into his face, pulling away while Bob said:

— Christ, Austen, you could've got us one.

— Yeah, and I'd never see the money again, Bob. I want a fiver for the petrol before I take you home, he'd said.

Bob dumped his gear in a swim near Austen, just to keep him from getting too scared in the dark. I wandered on till the track became overgrown and I sensed the back end of the pit, a broad channel in a blotted-out moon, overhanging bushes. I unrolled the sleeping bag and got in it, head spinning, hypnogogic faces rushing from the darkness.

I woke at dawn from fitful sleep and tackled up in a cold wet mist, flicked a single black-eyed pea under a bush twenty yards across the channel, brewed some coffee and rubbed my eyes. Half an hour later I hit a slow take and landed a nice common, a wake-up fish. I slipped it back and took Bob a cup of coffee. He was just coming-to, woken by all the cluttering and cursing a few swims down, Austen waking from a nightmare, or into one of his own production. Frantic reeling and casting, reeling and casting like he was trying to save his drowning dog or his sinking BMW. When he heard us talking he ran round, crashing through the bushes.

— Where's mine then? Okay, I bet I get one first, he said.

— Too late, Austen. Dexter's 'ad a nice double.

— Don't believe it.

— Smell my net then, I said.

— What on? he said.

— Black-eyed bean, I said.

— Bollocks, he said. Did you see it, Bob?

— No, I didn't have to.

— Well it's not true then. You have to have a witness or it doesn't count.

When the mist cleared me and Bob started to walk round the lake. It was fenced in, but Austen had let himself through with a key. The notices were everywhere. KEEP OUT. NO FISHING. THIS LAKE IS DANGEROUS. IT IS DUE TO BE FILLED IN, BY ORDER.

The next lake was a few miles away. A windy Saturday gravel pit for windsurfers. Austen was going to catch a thirty under our noses, in front of our very eyes, or behind our back and in your face up our arse. Again he bagged first swim and said this time we weren't his guests. If anyone came along and asked for our membership cards he didn't know us, we were poachers.

He put his waders on and out he went with the maples dustbin, a friggin St Bernard come to rescue carp angling. For an hour he sowed the water in front of him with fermented peas, by hand, catapult, and eventually just by tipping the dustbin upside down. Bob walked two miles to the nearest shop while I warmed up my only tin of soup, then tried to sleep. About three in the afternoon Bob came back looking like he'd seen a beneficent ghost. There was a nine-month bulge under his Richard Brautigan suit.

— You won't believe this, he said, unbuttoning his jacket enough for me to see the top of a big glass jar full of pills.

— Where's the grub? I said.

— Oh right, sorry, oh damn, I never got to the shop. I saw this really sweet little cottage, all overgrown with roses and creeper, you know, an' this old greenhouse and some apple trees. It was just like my aunt's place in Wales. I only went in for some apples, then, ah you know, I just fancied a peep in the window, saw it was like not empty but ... well I felt like Snow White.

Snow White found the bears' porridge, not 10kgs of gangland Valium. Bob insisted it was all 'in the clear'. The bloke obviously didn't need them. He was dead. Well, he must've died. They must've taken him away.

I said:

— What stopped the old bloke nipping out down the corner shop? Lots of cranks live in overgrown cottages. Might be an old woman, even. The district nurse.

— No, really, you'll understand when you see the sick room.

It was like he said, abandoned in the midst of life, the story well told by the garden, the unpicked beans, the fallen blackened tomatoes, the bramble at the door, the nettles on the window ledge. In the haste of departure, someone forgot to lock the door. The doctor, the ambulance crew, the undertakers. The sick room was upstairs, all stainless kidney bowls and queasy sheets, the smell of sweat gone by, of dying groans petered out and cobwebbed over. The cash-and-carry medicine spoke of the valetudinarian alright. Maybe a retired chemist who ran his own sickroom, stocking up for a wrongly estimated convalescence. There were enough medicaments to run a hospital for a week, or keep this man alive till doomsday. The pharmacology tomes may have been the labour of the amateur, or the retired professional's working knowledge.

Bob was pretty pharmacological too, dispensing, counting, weighing, dividing, identifying the labels and quantifying the doses. His reasoning was expanding the possibilities with each new hoard. I said:

— Christ, Bob, we're gonna need Austen's bait dustbin to cart this lot home.

— Yeah, he said, that's the idea. If we dump all our bait we can use the bait buckets.

I suppose we all share the same lust when discovering treasure, or simply a lot of anything for nothing. You always think: there must be something I can do with this lot. You despise the idea of someone else coming along, as if it's yours and always was. So you take the lot and there's never enough and never anything you can do with it. Your twenty kilos of mushrooms begins to rot. A ton of chestnuts goes rock-hard. Metal rusts, plastic goes rindy. No one wants to buy a thousand plastic coat-hangers. Or tile hangers or even aircraft hangers. Never take the lot. Always leave eighty per cent and chance the regret for life.

Bob's initial desire had been to supplement his daily Valium intake, leaving aside a few milligrams of his prescription to save up and barter when his Methadone fell short. Then he saw the possibilities of hoarding and selling and solving his insomnia for a year. Of dipping his hands into the chest of golden tablets and running them through his *'all mine!'* fingers.

We found the old pharmacist's shopping bags and made off with the bullion. Austen was asleep after frying a steak on his camping Gaz. I made some tea and chewed some grass from sheer hunger while Bob dumped his bait and washed his bucket. He didn't get many in the five-litre Dulux Brilliant White. So he said maybe he could roll the pills up in his sleeping bag. Trouble was Austen still had a few hookbaits in the bottom of his dustbin and it reeked enough to ruin the pills. In the end Bob just tipped the fifty litres of pills in his dossbag and said he'd bloody make sure Austen gave him a lift right to his front door.

I remember the night so well. Carp-wise I'd been on a roll elsewhere, taking fish everywhere that summer, Walthamstow, River Lee, Epping Forest, even Bowyers. But I felt no confidence at all in this pit. True there was a stiff wind in the afternoon and a healthy froth on the waves, but it was infested with windsurfers, the yuppie ones, ignoring the buoys and falling off in your swim. Casting was pointless. We were staying near Austen in case he relented and gave us something to eat from his mobile larder. We were in the wrong place. The middle, the open bank, the rostrum for Austen to be spotted by talent scouts.

Around five the windsurfers began to thin to a handful of wisps, the ones who could stand up the longest, so I put my fishing hat on and staunched hunger with a roll up. Bob was firing out bait into the swim. I walked round to the beach, a nice sandy disembarkation point for the nautical variety. It was thirty yards long and marked at each end by a fence and brambles, some alders running out about ten yards on banked up spits. The water was all churned up by wind and feet. I fetched a rod and plumbed the depth at ten yards. Five feet. The water was warm. I moved the gear and waited under a tree, waited till the last windsurfer went home, setting up and longing for sleep.

Austen had an early night. The wind dropped and the sky cleared. A cold moon like a bottle of milk out the fridge hung behind some streaks of cloud. Bob was sitting upright on his bed chair smoking and playing with his beard. I put the rods in the middle of the beach and placed the baits ten yards out to right and left, each on a rug of black-eyed peas. I waited an hour then fell asleep, the cold up my back, head still spinning with famine, heart like an old harmonium round the Almshouses. I knew I'd get a take, and I knew I'd lose it.

The run woke me up, a long low buzz on the old Herons. I was too far from my rods. Tangled in army groundsheet cape, catching the tongue of my boots as I horned in my foot, scuffing in a trail of wet laces, barking my knuckle on the churning reel pick-up, feeling the blood run out immediately. It was a big fish too, just tearing off, outwards. The clutch was jammed and I had to back-wind so fast it was like a starter motor which wouldn't catch, or transmission wind-up. The line was grating too. 8lb Maxima. It wasn't that I felt unlucky, just out of my depth, out of my body even. Cold, hungry, tired, completely unable to take charge. I called to Bob, very feebly, like a child in bed calling his mother and saying: I wanna be sick. No Bob came. The fish kited to the left. I wound like a spring-loaded tape-measure and gained all the line back, but it kept kiting, saw the fence and went for it. The line rasped and parted. I was left trembling and humiliated, my hand sore and bloody.

Bob's eyes were like two fags on the go at once. He must've put his hands in the wrong bottle. The moon corpsed him and he could've been one of those petrified soldiers sitting in the mud that First World War poets often wrote about.

— You asleep?

Bob just said no, it was hard sleeping with fifty litres of Valium in your sleeping bag.

Chris McCully

Chris McCully (b. 1958) has been fishing for forty years. His angling publications include *Fly-Fishing: A Book of Words* (1993), *The Other Side of the Stream* (1997) and *Sketches with Fishing Rods* (2008). In 2006 he edited Ad Swier's *Passion for Pike*, and in 2009 will publish *Pike Lures* with The Medlar Press. Based now in The Netherlands, during the colder months he fishes for pike and during the warmer months for sea-trout in Ireland and Denmark. For much of his fly-fishing life he fished the river Wharfe in Yorkshire, and was a member of The Kilnsey Angling Club. He is a regular contributor to several angling magazines in both the UK and The Netherlands.

www.chrismccully.co.uk

An Anatomy of Feathers

I

In 1968 he tied a perfect Orange Partridge.

You'll know the fly. 'One of the Yorkshire spiders,' you'll murmur, knowing full well that whatever these patterns represent, it's not spiders. Drowned duns, perhaps – olives awash, wind-harried; or smaller stone-flies. 'February Red,' you say aloud. In 1968, and just as you have done, I rolled their names around on my tongue, words brittle and aromatic as dried thyme: Dark Watchet; Purple Snipe; Dotterel Dun; Dark Spanish Needle; Orange Partridge. This was the lexicon of Pritt and the uplands, the limestone, of gryke and clint, of river-pools disappearing underground, of cave and conduit. These were the names born in the places where the rivers have always gone to sleep, resting on their spine of England.

And in 1968 he tied a perfect Orange Partridge.

They're not easy to tie, these spiders. They look so simple: a snecked hook; Pearsall's Gossamer, in the appropriate shade, lapped down in touching turns from the hook eye and back to form the body; and then the subtle, soft head hackle – no more than three turns, a sort of shrug; and a whip-finish not in the usual place, behind the eye, but behind the fibrous splay of hackle, helping the strands to strut.

They're wisps, suggestive nothings: silk – fine as a hair – and a gauze of feather. These days I can run them up in a couple of minutes. In 1968, even forming the body of just one of these patterns cost me half an hour. Merely catching in the silk behind the eye took an effortful fumble, and half a dozen exasperated goes after the first failures and unravellings. He took my hands in his, then: left hand holding the silk taut along the shank, while the right hand whipped back over the taut length ... over ... under ... over ... under ...

The bobbin of silk unspooled under the slightest of tension, millimetre by millimetre. Fingers tense with boy-sweat stained the orange to umber. It didn't matter, he said. The orange thread, when dry, was far too bright – what sort of insect has a body that shade? – so umber was better anyway. And there: the body was complete, an umber sliver. I tied a half-hitch in the silk, let the bobbin dangle, and wiped my fingers on the white tablecloth.

He was precise like that – precise in everything.

The trick is to prepare the feather.

What is a feather? A feather's ... a feather – something to do with poultry and pillows. Yet he showed me that feathers, and in particular the individual fibres of feathers, aren't merely a colour or texture. They have a structure. Every fibre of each individual feather is held together by miniature dynamics – by the fact that each single fibre of each single feather is participating in a set of relationships. Far from being poultry and pillows, feathers are adjacency and anatomy.

Feathers are a mesh of hooks.

You can see this under a hand-held magnifier. Look along the leading or trailing edge of any feather fibre and you'll see the serrations that make adjacent fibres into a web. It's this fact that allows feathers to retain their structure, even when wet. It's this fact which allows birds to fly. It's this fact which allows the salmon fly-dresser to construct brilliantly coloured feather wings where different fibres, belonging to plumage from different birds, are zipped into each other like shreds of Velcro under the tier's dextrous fingers. The metaphor is that the fibres are married.

Back then, knowing nothing of salmon flies with married wings, I married partridge feathers.

To tie a perfect Orange Partridge you need a well-marked breast feather. Feathers with a grey list work well, but those with a brownish tint work even better, since the fibres are if anything even softer, the marking and striations on the fibres even more insect-like. Strip off any downy fibres from the base of the feather, revealing the white quill. It's this quill which is held in the bird's flesh. Now hold the feather by its tip – the non-quill end. Note that the fibres have a set: they're splayed backwards from the quill, pointing towards the tip of the feather like a multiple, densely meshed set of aircraft wings. With a wetted thumb and forefinger, stroke the fibres back from their original set. This makes the fibres stand out from the hackle stalk. Notice, too, how the wetted fibres stick together, largely because they're hooked to each other by the feather's original dynamics.

Moisten the extreme tip of the feather, then take six or seven fibres on either side of the stalk's thinnest end and stroke them into a point. Holding this newly made and moistened point in one set of fingers, with the other set of moistened fingers stroke the fibres on either side of the quill so that they stand, completely symmetrically, at right-angles to it.

In your fingers will be a partridge feather, prepared for tying-in. The fibres at the tip of the feather will form a moistened point – like the finest of paintbrushes; the main fibres of the feather will be lying, meshed, at right-angles to the stalk, and will be absolutely equally disposed at each side of it; and the butt-end of the stalk will be a stripped bit of white quill.

You can test whether this feather is viable for its new purpose. Hold it up, and allow it to drop. If it sails, untwisting, gentle, rocking in a single plane as it drops then it's a good feather; if it spins like a sycamore seed then either the feather's structurally unbalanced or (more likely) your clumsiness has unbalanced it, particularly where the fibres on either side of the quill haven't been prepared symmetrically.

There at the kitchen table we played with partridge feathers for minutes which stretched into hours. (Half a crown, it was, for the one whose feather sailed most gently. He won, of course – and gave me the half a crown.) Then, at last, he finished the fly I'd begun earlier that evening – tied in the tip of the feather, gripped the butt-end of the quill in hackle pliers, and wound three turns of the feather as a hackle. He wound two turns of the silk back through the hackle to secure the stalk, then completed the fly by a whip-finish – three turns – snugged into the rear base of the hackle. Out came a needle; off came the top of a tiny bottle of varnish; drop of lacquer on the hackle-base finish, and …

He took the fly out of the vice, placed it in my open palm.

It was one of the most perfect things I'd ever seen.

Then and only then he took the fly-box out of his pocket. It was a tiny aluminium Wheatley, with·clips on two leaves. He opened the box.

'There, you see – Dark Spanish Needle… And there: Yellow Partridge. And there: Waterhen Bloa… 'bloa' means blue-grey, slaty… And there – watch it! – Dark Watchet… And here…'

There was one clip unfilled. Into the clip he placed the perfect Orange Partridge he'd just tied.

I had wanted things before that evening. Fry's Chocolate Cream; a Hornby 00 signal-box; a scale model of Jim Clark's 1967 Lotus – these were the sorts of things one could want. And yet even in that sort of wanting I hadn't realised quite what wanting was. What wanting was, was wanting a fly-box just like that, and wanting the skill to fill it with flies just like the ones he'd tied to fill his. I needed – no, I wanted, with all its double meanings of lack – the techniques, the easiness with the names, the insects, the rivers and the trout.

It wasn't just a form of greed, a rage for acquisition.

He'd taught me how to want to understand.

The following Christmas there was his unmistakable hand-writing on two dockets attached to two presents. 'For Chris…'

I undid the larger of the two wrappings. It was a field guide to the birds of Britain and Europe. If I look up from this desk, now, forty years later, as I pause from writing, I can see the same book on a much-used part of the reference bookshelf.

I undid the smaller of the two presents.

It was a Wheatley aluminium fly-box, identical to his, and empty.

I still have the fly-box, too. In its long, strenuous and complex life it has held spiders, small sea-trout flies, and still-water buzzers, but now again holds those Yorkshire spiders whose structure he taught me to begin to understand all those years ago. I've always kept one clip of the box empty, because… Why, then? Superstition? Tribute? Love?

It's simpler.

In 1968 he tied a perfect Orange Partridge.

II

It was years before we actually fished together. He disappeared into his own busy life, a life that comprehended a much-loved family and a large garden. But somehow, although he'd disappeared, he was always there. He was the memory in my fingers as I tied flies, the trust, the final reassurance. The little Wheatley box filled up.

If we're lucky, then even as it hurtles past, time somehow waits for us. It waits for the occasions and places in which we can begin to join ourselves up.

Time waited for us, then met us at the Wharfe.

I'd fished the Wharfe many times before I finally fished it with him. The upper river, with its green-grey clarity, its whitened rock terraces, its torrential pools, gives way to the relatively quieter reaches at Kilnsey, Grassington, Appletreewick – and below them, at Bolton Abbey. Here there are reaches of rock-fall, or glides sculpted from water held in limestone below overarching trees. In summer, when the sun's at its zenith, the water gives back movement to the clouds: the river is less a presence than a view. Here, in these parts of the middle river, grayling begin to make an appearance, and are thereafter found downstream, all the way through Addingham, Burley, and down to Pool. Here I fished the trotted worm or maggot as well as the fly. Here …

Here were all the moments that made up the fishing days. These days, caught in the different moments of Now, I often ask myself where home is. Is home here, in these notes, these books, this desk with its coffee-cup and clutter? True, this is a quotidian home, but home is also a set of imaginative alignments where one can feel at least briefly not … happy – no, not happy – but in place. And if I think of those alignments I don't think, or don't think immediately, of today's rooms with their faces and voices. I think of fishing. Ireland, then? Scotland? The august, manicured chalkstreams? The brawl of peat-stained water clearing after a late summer flood?

No. Always, on the edge of sleep, I go back to the Wharfe. He loved the dale, particularly the upper valley around

Langstrothdale, just as his father had loved it before him. There the river falls from the north-west watershed, and if you look up you see, always and everywhere, the slow movement of what Ted Hughes aptly described as the 'thin fastidious line that disciplines the fell'. Since this is the country of limestone, of cave and conduit, the river disappears in drought into cisterns deep in the rock, only to re-emerge in flood, when the very ground beneath your feet sounds with running water.

In spring the dark olives hatch, and the iron blues; there are needle-flies, the first stone-flies. The summer evenings bring on blue-wings and sedges. There are caddis everywhere. I often thought about writing, but never did write, that entomologist's diary of an angling season on the Wharfe, but one day, someone will – and will be astonished by abundance.

He came back to fishing later in life, and he came back to it on the upper river. As we walked some of the beats together he'd sometimes stop and point out a place where he'd con-structed a rope-swing over a pool sixty years before. 'We went swimming there. It's deep under that bank. The trout hide under the stones…'

He, too, was going back. Perhaps, towards the end, we all try to go back – to the places we loved, to our deepest alignments, to the places and voices that made us. In that respect I think that the crowds who gather to watch salmon making their own spawning migrations are responding to something that lies deeply within each one of us. We simply need, at the end, to go home.

'We used to play cricket here, you know.' I looked around at a mere strip of high grass lying at the water's edge high up the dale. He could sense the question before I asked it.

'We used to bring a lawn-mower. Put it in the back of the car. Mow a pitch. If you hit the ball over the river it was a six… Lost a lot of cricket balls, mind you. When we ran out, we'd have a picnic.'

He was going home, remembering, living at the last into his own deepest alignments. It wasn't just a matter of nostalgia. We didn't hang about the river moping on regret. Usually, we were far too busy trying to catch fish.

For three or four years, there at the end, we fished together regularly – so regularly that we began to feel even a touch proprietorial about what we'd come, quite wrongly, to think of as 'our' river. It was as if we were re-learning a private language, composed, as of old, of trust, of reassurance, of two pairs of hands tying a fly ... under ... over ... under ... over ... and of the day in 1968 when he tied a perfect Orange Partridge.

Proprietorial? Neither of us suffered fools, and in Thatcher's England there were plenty of new fools with plenty of new money. One early autumn day a shooting party turned up at the inn where we'd met for breakfast. None of them can have been over thirty. They were Londoners, and had hired guns, suits and Labradors for the occasion. They sat in the bar drinking, becoming louder with every tipple at the hip-flasks. They seemed to find the word 'duck' increasingly amusing. We left, and went in search of autumn sedges.

Towards lunchtime, fishing among random gunshots, I was concentrating, bent double for concealment, on a particularly tricky fish which had taken up feeding station under a coil of roots. Suddenly, upstream, there was a commotion in the water, and one of the shooting party lurched wetly towards me, putting down not only the trout I was stalking but any trout within a hundred yards. 'You seen a duck?' he asked – except he didn't ask. 'Seen a duck? Eh? Effin'dog can't find the effin' duck.' I told him, rather stiffly, that I had seen no duck, then reeled in and went in search of lunch.

As we opened the sandwiches he was looking particularly pleased with himself. I thought he'd probably got into a good fish. 'How did you get on?' There was a murmur in reply. I thought he hadn't heard. 'How did you ...?'

He opened his coat. Held there in the game pocket was a duck.

'Bloody fools. Shooting these ducks indiscriminately. They shot one, didn't mark it properly, and there it was, floating towards me. Quick work with the landing-net.' He smiled, but he was deeply saddened. Although 'bloody fools' was usually about as strong a criticism as he'd ever offer, I knew he found even the thought of those upper-class yobs deeply offensive, and their chosen ways of killing utterly unacceptable.

Gentleness, intelligence, charm, humour: those attributes, together with an understanding of how the country and all its land and river-scapes is put together, seemed even then to be vanishing from England, and as they vanished, England seemed to vanish too.

Never a hard word fell between us. The only time I ever found him even vaguely tetchy was towards the last days, when he was pumped full of blood-thinners and doctors' warnings. Mindful of the risks to him of even the slightest strain I kept picking up his landing-net as we walked between pools. Finally, just I was trying to help him over a stile, he paused and looked me straight in the eyes.

'I'm not a bloody invalid.'

He carried his own landing-net after that.

While he was going home, to the profundity of his first place, he was also choosing his own way back. In the face of medical head-shaking and grave counsels about an absolute minimum of fats and sugars he kept a secret cache of pork pies and Mars bars under a rug in the boot of the car. 'Can't go fishing without a growler,' he'd say, biting into something from Melton Mowbray.

He'd found his own way through Burma and the war; through families, friendships and fishing. Now he was choosing his own way out.

I let him.

The last time we fished together was on 23rd September, 1994. 'Warm and cloudy, light NE breeze,' says the diary. The Wharfe was low, and so we moved early in the evening to the Skirfare, whose Norse name means 'bright-flowing'. He got one fish by climbing into the fork of an overhanging tree and dibbing a tiny Crow Fly – an all-black scrap, tied with the herls of a feather he found by the river – onto an unsuspecting trout's nose. The diary notes that 'he's surprisingly good at being a tree,' and goes on to record that although I eventually got three trout on a dry John Storey ('Much hiding behind nettly hummocks and casting a long line upstream. 2lb. point, the last four feet of the leader well degreased…'), on that warm late summer evening we didn't fish much, but merely sat in the grass and waited for the sedges, and perhaps the hatch of blue-winged olives, that would eventually take place. And then we weren't even waiting. We just sat there, content in each other's company.

He knew, I think. In different ways we were both heading into the dark. Hindsight is always tricky, but – yes, I know he knew, because after that long, companionable silence up at Hawkswick he very gently said this:

'You can talk to me about anything, you know.'

I never did.

III

The story as I had it was that on his last day as himself he drove, with his ill heart, not to the hospital as one would have expected. That is, he did drive to the hospital, but only later.

With his ill heart he drove first to the Wharfe.

He wanted – I'm quite sure he wanted – one last glimpse.

And then there was no glimpse, all the reflections scattered, the views were lost, the memories fragmented, and all the lights went out.

Days later we all stood in the church, too stricken to sing. 'He leadeth me beside the still waters,' we mumbled. 'All things bright and beautiful…'

I thought of standing with him on Conistone Bridge, and watching the dippers busy in the shallows downstream. He loved dippers. 'Sturdy, independent little birds,' he said.

Where do you go and what do you do, after and beyond the rituals of grief? Eventually, after the sandwiches have been eaten and the faces and voices have gone home, you are left with yourself, and there in the first bereaved moments no one can imagine they're anything other than diminished.

Because I didn't want to feel, I worked. Then, like a fool, I drank. Then I repeated the cycle.

That autumn, I worked on a poem for him – a poem which would eventually appear in *Not Only I*. I tried to include in the words the water-plants, the dippers, the Wharfe's creased currents and the purl of its evening murmur, and I tried to set him there in the middle of it all. That is, I tried too hard, and the result is over-precise and over-worked. Meanwhile, I thought back, and often, to the evening in 1968 when he tied a perfect Orange Partridge, and between vodkas I tied some precise, over-worked and over-hackled Orange Partridges, too – stripping the fluff from the quill, stroking the point fibres to a tip, moistening the main webs of feather…

My heart wasn't in it.

I was working to try and find gratitude, but if I felt anything at all, it was the hangover which held all the selfishness of loss. At last, after months of trying to find the words and structures, and finding nothing but the vicious failure of myself together with anger, all of whose words meant Me, I gave up.

By then it was Christmas. I spent that Christmas, by choice, on my own. I couldn't bear the cheerful voices on the radio, the television. I didn't want the kindness which surrounded me, nor did I wish to inflict myself on it. I didn't know what to do.

If only because the alternative was the rage which had already settled at the bottom of the next bottle of vodka, I picked up the manuscript page of the poem I'd already abandoned, settled the dog in the back of the car, and drove back to the Wharfe, having to bite down hard to keep my eyes from swimming with tears. I pulled in the car just above the Skirfare bridge, trugged on a hat and a pair of boots, and walked down to the pool at Watersmeet, where the Skirfare coils itself into the main river.

The dog went off into the frost on a trail of his own, into his library of smells. It was a bitterly cold day – too cold as yet for snow – and windless. A dipper aimed upstream. Dead summer foliage, wearing fibres of ice on long-dead stems, looked as if it had been cast in bronze. The two rivers, the Skirfare and the Wharfe, held that almost luminous green clarity they carry at the year's midnight. On the far bank, over the pool at Watersmeet, the end of the rope-swing hung green with damp, and frayed.

I've sometimes thought that in our passages through time perhaps we leave some stain on the air where we have been once most happy, some relict of sensation. But on Christmas Day 1994 at Watersmeet there was nothing and no one – only the low-voiced winter rivers, and far away over the wood the rough calls of rooks.

There was a kind of dismissal everywhere.

I had one last, pointless duty to undertake.

I called in the dog, made him stand there in the shingle at the edge of Watersmeet. I took off my hat, fumbled with cold-clumsy fingers for the piece of manuscript paper in a jacket pocket. I'd called the poem 'Kingfishers' – a self-conscious pun.

'To look upstream to see that flash of flame/ and cobalt blue ...'

But there was no kingfisher, and the words of the opening lines fell into the Christmas silence like pebbles clanging into the base of a bucket. '... On Watersmeet,' I read, 'the Stepping Stones ...'

And everywhere was winter, vanishings and dismissal.

I got through the words without stumbling, folded the paper back into my pocket, put the hat back on, brought the dog to heel. It had started to snow – just the first flake, six-petalled, unique and miraculous, falling slowly past the trees at the lower end of the pool tail. One snow-flake, rocking gently down the air. Except it was no snow-flake.

There, like a weightless seed, unspinning, its fibres splayed, prepared, and its tip still moist from finger-spit ... It landed at my feet very softly, at the water's edge, and lay with its white hackle stalk convex against the surface.

These are the goodbyes. Time has happened, and all the changes have come true. But what's most true is the memory of the evening in 1968 when he tied a perfect Orange Partridge. And you are just a man standing at Watersmeet one Christmas Day many years ago, watching a feather floating on a river.

Copyright information

The Last Trout © John Galligan.

Back Waters © Colin Higgins.

First cast at the Loch of the Green Corrie and *A Bourach on Loch na Gainmhich* © Andrew Greig.

Tunnyland (excerpts) © John Andrews.

Pond Life 1, Pond Life 2 and *Brass Carp* © William Wyatt.

Fish Running © David Knowles.

The Stepping Stones, Between Honey and Salt and *The Wilderness Cure* © David Profumo.

Carp-horse Bob and *Bob Down Valium Valley* © Dexter Petley.

An Anatomy of Feathers © Chris McCully.

179

Two Ravens Press is the most northerly literary publisher in the UK, operating from a six-acre working croft on a sea-loch in the north-west Highlands of Scotland. Two Ravens Press is run by two writers with a passion for language and for books that are non-formulaic and that take risks. We publish cutting-edge and innovative contemporary fiction, non-fiction and poetry.

Visit our website for comprehensive information on all of our books and authors – and for much more:

- browse all Two Ravens Press books by category or by author, and purchase them online, post & packing-free (in the UK, and for a small fee overseas)

- there is a separate page for each book, including summaries, extracts and reviews, and author interviews, biographies and photographs

- read our regular blog about life as a small literary publisher in the middle of nowhere – or the centre of the universe, depending on your perspective – with a few anecdotes about life down on the croft thrown in. Includes regular and irregular columns by guest writers – Two Ravens Press authors and others

- sign up for our monthly e-newsletter, filled with information on our new releases and our authors, with special discounts, prizes and other offers.

www.tworavenspress.com